ABOUT CHEMISTRY

ABOUT CHEMISTRY

MAGNUS PYKE

B.Sc., Ph.D., F.R.I.C., F.R.S.E.

OLIVER AND BOYD

EDINBURGH AND LONDON

1959

OLIVER AND BOYD LTD
Tweeddale Court, Edinburgh 1
39A Welbeck Street, London W1

FIRST PUBLISHED 1959

PRINTED IN GREAT BRITAIN BY
HAZELL WATSON AND VINEY LTD
AYLESBURY AND SLOUGH
FOR OLIVER AND BOYD LTD., EDINBURGH

Acknowledgements

I should like to acknowledge the kindness of my friend Dr R. B. Strathdee, of the University of Aberdeen, in reading through the manuscript of this book. His comments and criticisms were most welcome. I should also like to acknowledge the assistance of Dr Neil Campbell, of the University of Edinburgh.

Figs. 25, 27 and 28 are reproduced by permission of the McGraw Hill Book Company Inc., Fig. 30 by permission of the Union Carbide International Company and Fig. 47 by permission of the Editor of *Discovery*. Fig. 31 is based on a photograph supplied by the British Petroleum Company.

I should also like to acknowledge the patient assistance of the publishers in guiding the manuscript through the press.

M. P.

Contents

1

What Chemistry is all About

Applied chemistry is today a predominant factor in modern life. For an up-to-date nation to have any hope of prosperity in the present competitive world it is essential for it to possess a vigorous and developing chemical industry. At almost every point in our daily activities we, the citizens of the twentieth-century world, enjoy the products of chemistry. The plastics from which our ball-point pens, our door knobs, our electrical fittings, the cockpits of our aeroplanes and half a hundred other things are made are due to modern chemistry. Nylon, terylene and a dozen other artificial fibres are chemical products. The special alloys that make many modern machines possible, special paints, high-octane fuels with specially designed anti-knock compounds in them, insecticides, weed-killers, anaesthetics and disinfectants—all these owe their existence to chemical science. The productivity of our land is in part due to our understanding of soil chemistry and to the manufacture of very large tonnages of chemical fertilisers. Synthetic rubber, dyestuffs and pharmaceuticals from coal are other successes of applied chemistry. Even many of the advances in medicine, such as the isolation of vitamins, the manufacture of antibiotics, the very knowledge of the mechanism of the living body, are due to chemistry applied to biological problems.

The great strides in chemical achievement often seem completely mysterious to people whose chemical education was restricted to a few rather perfunctory lessons at school or to a vague recollection that water is H_2O and sulphuric acid H_2SO_4. Sir Hector Hetherington, the Vice-Chancellor of Glasgow University—a classical scholar—once confessed in public that although he was taught chemistry for seven years as a boy he never had the least idea what it was really about.

There is, of course, a connexion between the sort of chemistry that people learn at school and the manufacture of petroleum from coal or the synthesis of vitamin C. And although no one must expect to be able to turn himself or herself into a qualified chemist by simply reading this book, I think that it is possible at least to set out the logical process of observation and thinking

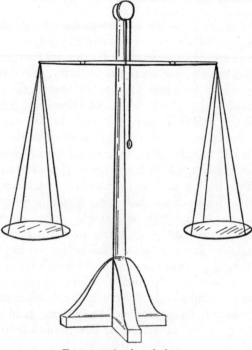

Fig. 1a.   Ancient balance

by which the trained chemist, who is heir to all the scientists who have lived before him, is able to do the things we see him doing today.

Chemistry is the science of the composition of matter. By science, we mean a particular kind of thinking. Science is in fact a philosophy. There are many people who work at scientific jobs from 9 a.m. in the morning until 5.30 p.m. in the evening without ever realising this. Some schoolmasters may know that science is a philosophy, but not all of them tell this to their pupils. It is because of this that so many people in later life feel completely mystified as to how each succeeding marvel of industrial chemistry comes about. They do not grasp on what principles the results are reached. Basically, science

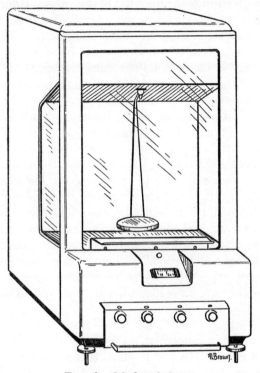

FIG. 1b. Modern balance

depends on the collection of facts. If the scientist is to do very much with his facts, they must be observed and measured quantitatively. The basic tool for the chemist is a machine for making accurate weighings. The modern chemical balance is a direct development of that used by the early Egyptians and Assyrians who are known to have been able to weigh accurately and had invented balances and sets of weights good enough for goldsmith's work. The balance used today can weigh quickly and accurately to four places of decimals of a gramme, which is itself about one twenty-eighth of an ounce. Fig. 1 illustrates a modern instrument side by side with an ancient balance.

The apparently complicated tools of the present-day chemist are all, almost without exception, designed to measure in quantitative terms the qualities of the various components of matter that non-scientific people merely describe. The basic quality is weight. From a thousand kilograms, which is about a ton, to a kilogram which is two and one-fifth pounds, to a gramme and so on to a milligramme which is, as its name implies, one-thousandth part of a gramme, is merely a record of weight measured with increasing precision. Length can be designated with equal accuracy from a kilometre, which is five-eighths of a mile, to a centimetre representing about two-fifths of an inch, or right down to measurements of the wavelengths of different-coloured light in Ångström units each of which is one ten-millionth of a centimetre. The chemist, like all other scientists, weighs and measures what he sees. Then, having obtained his records, he considers them and thinks what they mean. And the prime axiom of science is that there are always regularities in nature. These regularities can be called the "laws of science." Advances in science come when a man, considering the facts he has observed, suddenly appreciates that they are linked together in some systematic way.

Analysis

The chemist is concerned, as we have said, with the composition of matter. His first interest, therefore, has been to find out what are the components that make up the world he sees around him. And the separation of the mixed ingredients of common substances into their basic components, when it is systematically done, can be dignified by being called chemical analysis.

The beginnings of chemical analysis were probably the separation of metals from their ores by the Egyptians and Assyrians. The first metal that the Egyptians used was gold. Gold exists as such in nature and its separation, therefore, merely required observation and diligence rather than chemical knowledge. These early peoples, however, quite soon developed the art of smelting. This involves recognising ores, mining them, separating the rocky parts from the mineral, reducing them to fragments of the right size and heating them with enough draught to attain the required temperature but not enough to re-oxidise the metal. From very early times a great body of

FIG. 2.   Primitive still

practical knowledge was collected which made it possible for those who possessed it to recognise and recover from their ores six different metals, namely gold, silver, copper, tin, lead, and later, iron.

Everything he can find out about the separate components of matter is of interest to the chemist. The colour and appearance of different kinds of ore are properties to be noted, just as is the fact that they can be smelted by a special type of heat process. In dealing with liquids, one of the first characteristics to be studied was the manner in which components of mixed fluids could be separated by distillation. This is still today a basic analytical procedure. In the fermentation industries it may be necessary to analyse a mixed solution of alcohol and water, or something more complicated, for example a watery solution containing two organic solvents, say acetone and butanol.

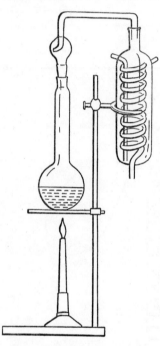

FIG. 3. Modern distillation apparatus

A typical piece of apparatus for separating mixtures of different liquid substances is shown in Fig. 2. This was used continuously by chemical practitioners from the first century A.D. right up to the middle of the nineteenth century. The material under examination is placed in the "body," into which the "head" is fastened by a paste, such as flour and water. The "head" serves to condense the vapours which run down the glass into the gutter and flow through the "beak" or "nose" into the receiver. When a watery solution of alcohol is to be analysed, the first vapours to come off when the sample is heated consist principally of alcohol, which is thus separated by the procedure.

In Fig. 3 I have shown a modern apparatus, to be found to this very day in the laboratory of any distiller, for analysing the content of spirit in his fermented wort.

Before a chemist can begin to think reasonably, systematically and logically about the components of matter, he has to have means that are at least moderately precise for recognising what he is dealing with. His method of recognition and measurement is analysis. And to start with, analysis is quite

empirical. Iron, for example, is the sort of stuff it is because
. . . it is the sort of stuff it is. Botany, like chemistry, is also a
science. It is, of course, a branch of biology. Botanists recognise
what plants they are dealing with by means of a key. This
botanical key goes something like this:

			If discription applies, turn on to paragraph number . . .
Para. No.	1	Leaves divided into separate leaflets	2
		Leaves not divided into separate leaflets	8
Para. No.	8	Leaves lance-shaped, about $\frac{1}{2}$ in. broad, spine tipped	Chile Pine
		Leaves not as above	9
Para. No.	9	Leaves less than $\frac{1}{4}$ in. broad, needle or scale like	10
		Leaves more than $\frac{1}{4}$ in. broad, not needle or scale like	18
Para. No.	18	Leaves opposite on twig	19
		Leaves alternate on twig	24
Para. No.	24	Evergreen trees or shrubs with spiny leaf-margins	25
		Deciduous trees or shrubs with toothed, entire or lobed leaf-margins	28
Para. No.	28	Leaves lobed	29
		Leaves entire or toothed	34
Para. No.	29	Leaves with stalks less than 1 in. long	30
		Leaves with stalks 1 in. or more long	31
Para. No.	30	Tree 30–40 ft. high, red berries	Hawthorn
		Tree 60–120 ft. high, acorns	Oak

There is no special reason for an oak leaf to be scalloped and
that of an ash in separate strips. The botanist merely notes that
this is so. Similarly, an analytical chemist takes an unknown
material and looks at it. Then he may dissolve it in water or
perhaps in nitric acid. To this solution he adds hydrochloric
acid. If a cloud of solid particles appears and settles to the
bottom as a precipitate, this means that silver, mercury or lead
is present. How does he know? He knows because these
"Group I metals," as they are called, behave like this, in just
the same way as an oak tree has scalloped leaves. The chemical
key is operated like the botanical one. If hydrochloric acid has

no effect, the analyst can try bubbling in hydrogen sulphide gas. A black precipitate shows that mercury, copper or bismuth is there, a yellow precipitate indicates cadmium or arsenic, and a brown one antimony or tin. If there is no effect at all from the hydrogen sulphide, the chemist goes on a stage further with his key until eventually he ends up with something he can recognise.

These are the sorts of procedures that chemists use in order to identify the different varieties of materials with which they deal. By this I mean that the different components of matter are identified by properties that can either be perceived directly such as colour, sheen, consistency or relative weight, or by properties that can be discovered by chemical manœuvres, that is, whether a substance will dissolve in water, whether it will burn, whether it will dissolve in acid and if it does whether hydrogen sulphide gas makes it precipitate again, at what temperature it melts when it is heated, and so on. But besides needing to recognise the different substances of which matter is composed, the chemist wants to know how much of each is present. In other words, he must develop a system of quantitative analysis.

Although a good deal of theory about the mathematics of physical chemistry and much else has been worked out in recent years, basically, quantitative analytical chemistry is an extension of the qualitative procedures by which the analyst recognises what he has got. Substances behave as they do because that is the way they behave. Fortunately, however, just as oak leaves are always lobed, so the calcium "ion" is always precipitated by oxalate in neutral solution. It is this constancy of natural behaviour which is the basis of science. But, first of all, the scientist must learn about this natural behaviour. When he has learnt how substances behave, he can, when carrying out a quantitative analysis, take common-sense steps to ensure that he performs his operations so precisely that he can calculate from his measurements— whether they be of weight or volume or colour—exactly how much of the substances he is interested in is responsible for whatever has happened.

For example, we have said that calcium is precipitated from solution by oxalate. In order to find out how much calcium there is in a particular sample the analyst first weighs very carefully, usually to four places of decimals, the amount he takes. He may then dissolve this in an appropriate solution to which he will add oxalate. A precipitate of solid granules is formed by the calcium (if any calcium is there). The analyst

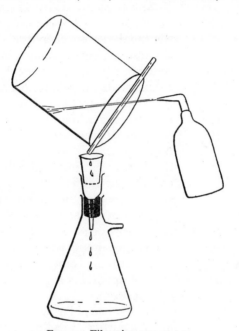

FIG. 4.   Filtration apparatus

wants to recover this and weigh it. First he filters the liquid through a funnel with a finely perforated bottom. Fig. 4 shows how he uses a fine stream of water to wash every particle of the precipitate on to the filter. Then he dries it by putting the funnel into an oven. When it is dry, he weighs it and from the weight recorded can calculate how much calcium it represents.

This is called a "gravimetric" method. Such methods can be used for silver, for copper, for magnesium and, indeed, for a large number of substances. In principle, the methods are simple and direct. In practice, of course, the chemist needs to know quite a lot about the behaviour of different materials. Information of this sort has been accruing for a very long time, from the early period of the alchemists to the present day.

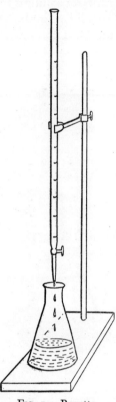

An alternative method of analysis is called "volumetric." Many familiar substances, chalk, say, or bicarbonate of soda, neutralise acids. To measure the amount of these present in some mixture, the analyst can therefore dissolve his accurately weighed sample in a precisely measured volume of acid of known strength. An amount of this acid exactly proportional to the amount of chalk or bicarbonate in the sample will be neutralised. The analyst can then measure how much acid is left by running in through his "burette," which is an exactly graduated tube, just enough standard alkali to neutralise the remainder of the acid. One way of knowing when this occurs is by the change in a coloured indicator, for example, red litmus turning blue. Fig. 5 shows the kind of apparatus required for this sort of procedure.

Another way of measuring the amount of some particular component in a chemical compound is by means of "colourimetric" analysis. As any schoolboy who has played with a Christmas "chemistry

FIG. 5. Burette

set" will know, certain mixtures give coloured solutions. A famous method for analysing phosphate depends on the fact that when mixed under appropriate conditions with a molybdenum-containing solution it produces a blue colour. The more phosphorus there is in the mixture, the bluer the colour will be. Consequently all the analyst has to do is to measure in quantitative terms how blue any particular blue colour is. Ten years ago or so, this was done by means of the sort of "colourimeter" illustrated in Fig. 6. The blue solution derived from the specimen being analysed was put into one cup of the instrument and a standard blue colour made from a known quantity of phosphorus was put into the other. A transparent glass plunger was dipped into each cup.

The operator looked down an eye-piece and saw an illuminated circle so arranged that one-half of the circle was the blue colour seen through the end of one of the glass plungers and the other half of the circle was the colour seen through the other plunger. He could then move one of these plungers up or down, thus looking through a deeper or shallower layer of the blue solution, until the colours seen side by side in his circle of vision exactly matched. The depth of liquid could then be read off a scale and the amount of phosphorus in the unknown solution calculated by comparison with the standard colour.

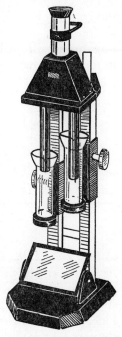

Some analysts were better at matching colours than others and in consequence their analyses were more accurate. Within recent years, the need to match colours by eye has disappeared and the comparison is made by means of a photo-electric cell. A modern "photo-electric absorptio-meter," as this instrument is called, is illustrated in Fig. 7.

FIG. 6.   Colourimeter

Colourimetric analysis has become very popular in modern chemical industry. A great deal of effort has been given to the discovery of dyes that will give special colours with different chemical substances. The different colours one sees are, as is well known, due to the different wave-lengths of light. By using specially chosen light filters, as is commonly done in photography, photo-electric cells can be made very discriminating in the light they measure. It is possible, therefore, to arrange a photo-electric instrument to measure in one mixed solution the amount of a number of different colours simultaneously and thus to record the amount of a number of substances in the original sample under analysis. All that the analyst needs to do is to put in the appropriate light-filter and read off the amount of the appropriate substance present.

The colour of a substance, or a colour produced by a substance when it combines with some other specific compound, is a property that, as we have just described, can be conveniently used to recognise whether the particular material is present, or to measure how much is there. Now "colour" need not strictly

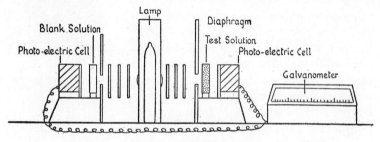

FIG. 7.   Absorptiometer

always be visible. The longest light wave-lengths that we can see with our unaided eye are those that give us the sensation of redness. As the wave-length gradually shortens we see the successive colours of the rainbow, red, orange, yellow, green, blue, indigo and violet. But although we can see nothing longer than red and nothing shorter than violet there are in fact invisible "colours" on either side, that are equally characteristic of a particular substance.

When you look at a liquid and it appears blue, what has actually happened is that the white day-light, which is a mixture of all the colours of the spectrum, has been blocked so that the liquid has absorbed all the coloured components except the blue. Only this wave-length passes through, and in consequence we see the liquid as blue. Instead of looking at a coloured solution by eye and measuring the amount of colour with a "colourimeter," as shown in Fig. 6, or getting a photo-electric cell to "look at" it in an "absorptiometer," as shown in Fig. 7, a chemist can pass a beam of rays containing both visible and invisible "light" through the solution and then record the amount and kind of absorption which occur due to the substances in the solution with an instrument called a "spectrograph" (Fig. 8). This instrument is so designed that a photographic plate records the spectrum of both visible and "ultra-violet" light and shows where the rays have been absorbed. I do not want to go into the details of how this is done. The important point is that it is simply a method of measuring a physical characteristic of a substance—its colour,

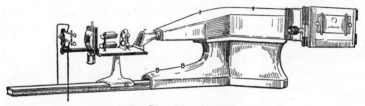

FIG. 8.   Spectrograph

in fact—and thus recognising and assessing the amount of the substance present.

Another way of identifying the components in a material by colour is to burn them and examine the colour of the flame. In its simplest form, this method of analysis can be done by putting the material into a gas flame, or heating it to incandescence in some other way, and simply looking at the colour in the flame. Salt thrown on to the fire gives an orange colour, showing the presence of sodium. The same yellow colour can be seen in "sodium lighting" on trunk roads. Mercury gives a purplish green, and potassium gives red. Although an analyst examining a small amount of an unknown substance might see what colour it gives in a flame, to do quantitative determinations he requires a spectrograph to identify each component more surely and to measure its amount. In the steel industry, where precise analyses of steels and alloys are required, and required very quickly, the basically simple though technically complex process of spark spectrography—that is identifying

and measuring constituents of the metal by their spark "colours"
—is now being done automatically. Phosphorus, silicon,
manganese, nickel, chromium, tin, copper, molybdenum,
aluminium, vanadium, titanium, lead and boron in an alloy
can be analysed in exactly five minutes. The sample of metal
to be examined is used as one electrode and an electric spark
is struck from it. The lines of the spectrum representing
the different elements to be measured are isolated by a spec-
trometer and pass through appropriate slits on to mirrors which
focus them on to photo-tubes. The light causes an electric
current to charge a condenser. At the appropriate moment the
exposure is automatically terminated; simultaneously, the
charging of all the condensers stops. A switch selects each condenser in turn and records the charge on each as a step on a
chart. The height of these steps shows the amount of each
element present. The machine contains as an added refinement
an electronic system for reproducing a facsimile of the written
record of the results.

The great machine that I have just described seems at first
glance to be complex and mysterious. But what it is in fact
doing is recognising and measuring the components of a substance by qualities only one step removed from colour. The
operation in fact epitomises the basic procedures of science.
That is, to measure exactly and to examine systematically
what the non-scientific person recognises only in general terms.
The layman would say that a solution of copper sulphate is
blue. The scientist would first measure in quantitative terms
how blue it is with, perhaps, the sort of instrument illustrated
in Fig. 6. But he can be more precise still if he next observes
the absorption spectrum of the blue solution. This can not only
give a measure of how much copper sulphate is present but,
since every substance has a characteristic power of absorbing
the different wave-lengths of the light of the spectrum, it also
identifies the actual substance being measured. Furthermore,
as we have seen, instruments can be designed to use the spectrum of wave-lengths either shorter or longer than those of
visible light. Fig. 9 is a diagram of the varying wave-lengths
available, ranging from the shortest of gamma rays, through

X-rays and ultra-violet and so down the scale to the long waves used for radio broadcasting.

Advances in scientific understanding have often had to wait upon developments in analytical techniques by which the components of matter could be recognised and measured with increased accuracy. For example, the standard method of measuring the amount of sugar in a solution makes use of the fact that when a liquid containing sugar is boiled with a solution of copper salts, part of the metallic copper is precipitated and can be filtered off and weighed. The analysis has to be done in an exactly standard way and the analyst needs to

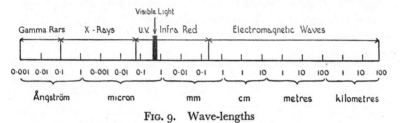

FIG. 9.   Wave-lengths

use vessels of a recognised size and must bring the liquid to the boil in an exactly uniform way or he will obtain an inaccurate result. The whole operation is rather difficult to do and a fair amount of sugar must be present if a precise answer is to be obtained. It was only when an improved analytical technique was developed that it became possible for medical scientists to make real progress in their studies of the disease, diabetes, which involves a disordered loss of sugar from the body and the consequent presence from time to time of harmfully large amounts of sugar in the blood.

This is an example of the importance of being able to measure by analytical means very small proportions of a substance in a mixture or compound. The amount of sugar in blood is normally very small, and for a long time its presence there at all was overlooked. But a different aspect of analysis which is often equally important is the need to determine the composition of very small amounts of material. When a new substance is isolated, for example, a vitamin or something like penicillin, at first there may only be a very small amount of it available. Methods of analysis that will work with very small samples may, therefore, be essential before any advance in knowledge is possible.

The most famous inventor of microchemical methods, as they were called, was Professor R. Pregl of the University of Graz in Austria. The chemical principles he followed were just the same as those used on a more normal scale. But he devised ways of weighing, of measuring volumes of liquid used to neutralise acids and alkalis, and of measuring colours of solutions, all on a tiny miniature scale. For example, the "pipettes" for measuring out minute amounts of liquid were glass tubes drawn out to the thinness of a toothbrush-bristle. Professor Pregl showed great ingenuity in designing what

FIG. 10.   Separating liquid by capillary attraction

almost seemed like dolls'-house apparatus for doing chemical analysis. He and a number of other workers, who have since developed the use of micro technique, have had to use a variety of ingenious methods for handling the very small quantities with which they deal. For example, quite complicated analyses are done using only a single drop of solution. This drop may be moved about by capillary force, that is the attraction that makes it run up narrow tubes or hang on to the underside of a microscope slide. Again, if the analyst wants to separate the liquid from a substance that he has precipitated in the bottom of a tube he can also do it by using capillary attraction (Fig. 10).

A much more elaborate type of apparatus is used for measuring the amount of nitrogen in a small sample of material. This equipment is very popular, which indicates, in science as in any other kind of activity, that it works well in spite of its complexity. It is illustrated in Fig. 11.

Many of the substances that occur in nature are closely

similar to each other and it has quite often happened that the progress of scientific knowledge has been held back until satis-

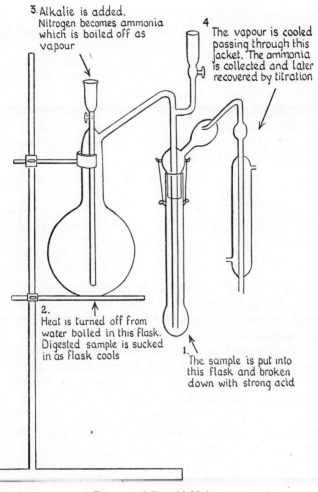

3. Alkalie is added.
Nitrogen becomes ammonia which is boiled off as vapour

4 The vapour is cooled passing through this jacket. The ammonia is collected and later recovered by titration

2.
Heat is turned off from water boiled in this flask. Digested sample is sucked in as flask cools

1.
The sample is put into this flask and broken down with strong acid

FIG. 11.   Micro-kjeldahl

factory methods of analysis have been worked out for separating similar materials and measuring the amounts of each. One of Louis Pasteur's first great discoveries depended on the obser-

vation that a particular substance, tartaric acid, that turned up
in the dregs in wine barrels, existed in two distinct chemical
forms. There were no methods of analysis available for
separating these, so Pasteur was compelled to do this laboriously
by hand, distinguishing the two kinds by differences in the
shape of their crystals.

The importance to science of new and delicate analytical
methods is demonstrated by the fact that the Nobel Prize, the
highest award there is for science, was granted to two young
men for developing an entirely new method of analysis. The
mathematics and physics involved in this method, called
"paper partition chromatography," are quite complicated, but
the practical operations are simple.

An analyst wanting to separate the two members of a mixture of, say, sugar and sand might use the obvious expedient of
seeing whether one component could be dissolved in water,
leaving the other behind. If the substances were more nearly
alike than sand and sugar he might see whether one was more
soluble in alcohol or chloroform than the other. Then, by
carrying out a series of extractions the proportion of one in the
solvent liquor could gradually be increased until at last the
other had been entirely left behind. The two chemists about
whom I am writing, Drs Martin and Synge, conceived the
notion of achieving the same effect as that of a long series of
extractions by arranging that the mixed solution of the material
under analysis should, as it were, cascade down a solid honey-
comb structure containing the extracting liquid in which one
component was more readily dissolved than the others. The
final stroke of brilliant ingenuity was the conception that this
honey-comb support could take the form of a sheet of blotting-
paper.

We have all seen the sort of thing that happens when a drop
of red ink is shaken on to absorbent paper. The circle of ink
enlarges and as it does so bands of different colours form. What
is happening is that the individual components of the mixture
of pigments in the ink are being separated one from the other.
The pigment most readily moved across the paper by the
advancing moisture is carried fastest while the others travel

behind at different speeds depending on their particular characteristics.

The way this principle is used in analytical chemistry is to apply to an absorbent paper a drop of liquid containing a very small amount of the mixture of substances it is desired to separate. The paper is then hung with its end dipping into an appropriately chosen mixture of liquids. These liquids gradually travel down the paper: it is usually arranged that this should take about eight hours. As the liquid travels it carries the components from the sample at different speeds. At the end of the time allowed the carrier liquid is dried off the paper. If the components being studied are themselves colourless, a chemical indicator is then applied, usually in the form of a spray, and the position of the various components can then be detected by the coloured stain each produces in reacting with the indicator.

Very small amounts of material can be analysed by this method of paper-partition chromatography. Fig. 12 illustrates how simple the technique is in operation. A mixture of different sugars needed to be analysed. A drop of the mixture was measured exactly by means of a micrometer syringe and was applied at a marked point in the middle of a ruled line at the top of the absorbent paper. Two other drops containing a series of known sugars were applied on the same ruled line one on each side of the drop of unknown sugar mixture. The paper was then hung in an airtight box with its top end dipping into the solution of mixed solvents. At the end of the eight-hour period, the paper was dried and cut into three strips, as shown in the figure. The two strips on the outside were sprayed with indicator and when the position of the various sugars had become apparent, the middle strip containing the mixture being analysed was cut up so that the parts where the known sugars would be were separated. These parts were then extracted individually with water so that the amounts of each different sugar—if it happened to be present in the mixture at all—could easily be measured by an ordinary titration.

This method of analysis, almost as soon as it was invented, was found to be applicable to all sorts of different substances. And it enabled separations to be carried out that had previously been very slow, laborious and inaccurate or even quite impossible to achieve before paper chromatography was available. The procedure described above is suitable when mixtures of, say, half a dozen substances are to be separated. When more complex materials are being analysed, for example different types of protein which may be composed of thirty or more

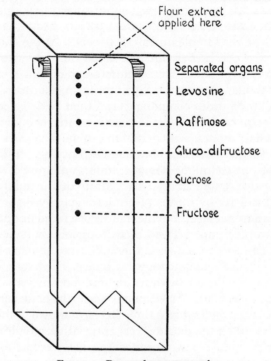

FIG. 12.   Paper chromatography

linked fractions, the process may be done in two parts. First, the fractions are spread downwards by a single running of a solvent mixture. The paper is then hung sideways and the fractions spread again across the width of the paper, and in a new order, by using a different mixture of solvent liquids. The whole technique, so simple in operation, even if the dynamics and mathematics of its theory are complex, has enabled a very considerable advance in chemical knowledge to be made in many different fields.

Great artists are in some ways very ordinary people. They look at the same things as we do and use the same kind of paint as any other painter, yet they see in a new and different way and enable us to see differently too. The same holds for the greatest among the scientists. Newton, Lavoisier, Pasteur or Hopkins each made enough new discoveries to establish not one substantial reputation but several. In the same way, the original publication by Drs Martin and Synge, which first described the idea of separating mixtures of similar substances by using two or more liquids in paper-partition chromatography, contained also an additional paragraph prophesying that the same kind of process could probably be used for separating mixtures of gases or volatile substances that could be readily vaporised. For ten years nobody had the wit to pay any attention to this suggestion until at last Dr Martin himself tried out the notion and triumphantly demonstrated that he had here another novel and extremely important advance in analytical chemistry.

The new technique is now called gas chromatography. The way it works is this. Instead of applying the measured drop of sample to a strip of paper, it is injected into a column which is kept at a fixed temperature by means of a heating-jacket. The warmth of the jacket vaporises the sample being analysed and it is then swept slowly along the column by a stream of some inert gas such as nitrogen. The mixture of components in the vaporised sample "bounce" along, bumping through the granules of packing with which the column is filled. These granules are wet with some specially selected liquid. Some of the mixed vapours of the sample cling to the wetted granules of the column packing more persistently than others and, in consequence, the components of the mixture become separated out as they jostle along to the end.

The analyst watches the end of the column and as each component emerges he records the time and the amount. If necessary, the separate fractions can be collected for identification, should the worker doing the analysis not know what they are.

One of the simplest and yet most elegant methods of recording the emergence of each separate substance in the mixture is shown in Fig. 13. A jet of hydrogen gas is burned at the end of the column and a sensitive electrical thermometer, a thermocouple, is mounted above the flame. The steady temperature is continuously recorded on a chart. When the first component of the sample comes through, it burns in the jet of hydrogen and the temperature of the flame increases. This increase appears as a peak on the chart. Analysis by gas chromatography is particularly useful, to choose an important modern example of applied science, in the new industry of petroleum chemicals. In this industry, a petroleum fraction is split up into a series of substances which are often somewhat troublesome to separate.

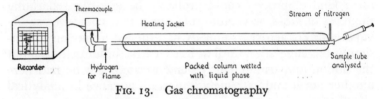

FIG. 13.   Gas chromatography

Gas chromatography quickly shows the operator what kind of mixture he has obtained. And if he wants to find out how much of each separate substance is present in his mixture, he can often do so by measuring the area of each successive peak on his chart.

In the ordinary, every-day, non-scientific world, we ordinary people get to know a good deal of rough and ready chemistry. That is to say, we learn by experience quite a lot about the chemical properties of different kinds of matter. For example, one is in a friend's house and comes across a little statue—a dog on the mantelpiece, let us say. "Hello! That's rather nice. I wonder what it's made of." We pick it up. Is it metal? No, it is too light and does not ring when we tap it. Is it wood? No, it is too hard. One cannot indent it with one's finger-nail. It's not plaster. Can it be glass? No, not hard enough. The only thing left—when we have finished applying our crude tests of the properties of the material—is to make up our minds that it must be one of the new "plastics"!

If we had been pressed we could have gone further with our everyday chemistry. By cutting a little chip off with a knife we could have found out whether it would burn and if so what kind of a smell it produced and whether it melted or charred or refused to burn at all. Analytical chemistry is merely the systematic use of the great mass of information that has been collected and recorded about the properties of different substances. And in order to make the most effective use of this recorded information, accurate instruments and tools have also been devised. Among these, the modern analyst has today the automatic "aperiodic" balance for making precise and rapid weighings, the photo-electric absorptiometer for measuring colours, and ultra-violet and infra-red spectro-photometers for measuring in accurate scientific terms properties allied to colour but beyond the limits of the human eye. Besides these individual instruments, chemists have at their disposal a vast catalogue of chemical properties which they know that different substances possess: the way that this or that material reacts with acids or alkalis or with particular reagent chemicals.

Lastly, the modern analyst can use a variety of special methods for separating the components of compounds and mixtures. And among the most sensitive and delicate of those are the new methods of paper-partition chromatography and gas chromatography.

During the autumn of 1956, a grand inquest was held by the Royal Institute of Chemistry to try to decide what a chemist ought to know and how to train him to know it. During this discussion, Professor Wheeler pointed out that in his opinion it was not essential any more for a chemical scientist to possess any high degree of manual dexterity. This comment called down a storm of disapproval from all sorts of chemists brought up in an older tradition. The progress of the age, however, seems to be proving that Professor Wheeler was right. Whereas it was once upon a time necessary for the analyst to be able, like an artist, to match colours through the eyepiece of a colourimeter, nowadays he can use a photo-electric absorptiometer that does the matching for him, precisely, quickly and automatically. Before, the chemist had to watch carefully in order to detect the exact drop of added acid at which his blue litmus paper (or whatever indicator he was using of whatever colour) turned red. To-day, he can use what is called a "direct-reading pH-meter," that does much the same job but records the end-point he wants on a dial.

The recognition of the different substances that make up the material structure of the world we live in is the first business of the chemist. Next, he must know how to measure the amounts of the ingredients of the compounds he finds and of the changed substances he makes from them. It is, indeed, upon this basis of facts and of their systematic relationships to each other that chemists have thought out the laws of nature that enable them to achieve their immense practical results. These practical successes are today based on knowledge, observation and thought rather than being dependent on manual dexterity. Indeed, quite recently several machines have been put on the market for doing chemical analysis automatically. One of these contains an electronic control unit that arranges for the apparatus to measure out for itself a sample, add to it in sequence the necessary chemical reagents, measure the resulting colour change or colour density or whatever may be the end result of the reaction, record the answer on a chart, wash itself out and then start all over again with a fresh sample.

The chemist, then, studies the nature of the ninety-two substances that make up everything on earth and finds out how they behave. Partly, he does this from the insatiable curiosity of the human mind. But partly, his motive is, of course, strictly materialistic. He wants to make something useful or agreeable or—as with gold—he wants to recover something valuable. He obtains his information by the kind of procedures I have briefly described. Let us go on now, therefore, and say something about what kind of substances the ninety-two elements* of the globe are.

---

* A number of new elements have recently been discovered by chemists using techniques developed by atomic physicists. Some of these elements are "artificial," inasmuch as they do not normally exist on earth, and some are evanescent and only exist for a second or two. The total number of known elements, including these, has at the moment of writing reached 102.

2

What Things Are Made of

All the material of the earth is made up, one way or another, from ninety-two different elements. From our present point of view an element may provisionally be defined as any homogenous stuff that cannot be separated into anything simpler by *chemical* means. Of course, in the light of modern knowledge of atomic structure, this definition is inadequate. It is a moot point whether we are defining what is meant by an "atom", or what is meant by "chemical." But I think that we can let it pass until later on.

All terrestrial matter is composed of ninety-two elements, and (we insist) the chemist as such is concerned solely with these. They sometimes occur alone as pure substances (for example carbon, iron or gold), or may alternatively be found in chemical combination one with another. Examples of compounds are chalk (calcium carbonate), water (hydrogen hydroxide) or Epsom salts (magnesium sulphate heptahydrate). It is a curious natural anomaly that compounds of two or more elements are often quite unlike the elemental substances of which they are composed, both in appearance and behaviour. It often takes the circumstantial evidence of chemical manipulation to prove that a compound is indeed made up of its separate elements, so different is it from any of them. Chemical compounds are, as it were, entities in their own right. They behave as such and, as we must discuss later, they are always made up of their component elements in one or more of certain arithmetical proportions. It is this comparative permanence of behaviour and composition that makes the difference between compounds and mixtures of compounds or elements. Whereas a chemist uses the word "compound" in a precise technical sense, his understanding of "mixture" is just the same as anybody else's. If one digs up some rock and crushes it, the broken pieces may be a mixture of all sorts of things. But among these may be some magnetite. This is a compound, in the strict chemical sense, and is always made up of a combination of three iron atoms and four oxygen atoms.

Since we are going to consider what sorts of useful things chemists do with the substances to be found on earth, it would perhaps be useful to review briefly what these ninety-two substances at his disposal are like.

We can tick off six of them quite quickly. These are helium, neon, argon, krypton, xenon and radon. Each of these is a very inert gas. None of them will burn or combine with anything except for a somewhat unexciting water-compound, xenonhexahydrate. Helium is a light gas, sometimes used for filling balloons, and found most plentifully in certain natural springs in the United States. Neon is heavier than helium and is used in some types of electric lamps. Argon is heavier again than neon and is also used—on accounts of its inertness—in electric bulbs. Krypton and xenon, each heavier than the last, are found together with neon and argon in very small traces in liquid air. Radon is the heaviest of all these six inert gases and occurs as an emanation of radium. The chemist does almost nothing with these substances because there is nothing they will do. (Atomic physics has something to say about helium, but we will come back to that later.)

The next group of elements is much more interesting. These are hydrogen, fluorine, chlorine, bromine, iodine and astatine. Leaving astatine out of account for the moment, each of these substances, which are listed in order of increasing weight, can exist as gases. Hydrogen is the lightest of all gases. It has no smell, it burns in air, and combines with oxygen to form water, of which compound it forms one-ninth by weight. (This last fact, it should be said, is one of the basic premises of chemical science.) It also combines with quite a large number of other elements. Fluorine, the second member of the group, is the most reactive substance known. It reacts with hydrogen, igniting as a red-bordered flame, and all sorts of other substances—carbon, silicon, phosphorus, sulphur—burn spontaneously in fluorine. Combined with hydrogen as hydrofluoric acid, it reacts with silicon; and for that reason hydrofluoric acid cannot be kept in glass bottles, as silicon is the principal component of glass. Chlorine as a gas smells rather like fluorine. It is also highly reactive but less violently so than fluorine. Combined with hydrogen it forms hydrochloric acid. Bromine, heavier than chlorine, forms a brownish gas, as distinct from the greenish colour of chlorine, and at ordinary temperatures is a heavy brown liquid (Fig. 14). Like the other

FIG. 14. Bromine liquid and gas

substances of this group it combines with many other elements. Iodine is heavier still. Its gas is purplish and it forms, not a liquid like bromine, but shining black metallic flakes. The commonest source of hydrogen is, of course, water. Fluorine and chlorine are plentiful in certain minerals (common salt, for example, is sodium chloride). Bromine and iodine, washed out of the earth, are recoverable from sea water. The heaviest member of the group, astatine, is little more than a research curiosity. In general, it resembles iodine and is, it seems, concentrated in the thyroid gland of guinea pigs, just as iodine is.

Another group of substances with which chemistry deals includes two of the key elements: oxygen and sulphur. Oxygen is a gas, the component of air that enables us to live and, indeed, enables all combustion to occur. It is the opposite pole to hydrogen of that ultimate substance that makes the world what it is, namely water. Oxygen combines with all things that burn, as we usually understand that term. Sulphur, heavier than oxygen but of the same group, is the brimstone of antiquity. It combines with many other elements to form sulphides, just as oxygen forms oxides. And just as higher living creatures live by oxygen, so certain special organisms can live by using sulphur in their vital biochemical processes. The still heavier members of the "oxygen group" are in order, selenium and tellurium. These occur in some Japanese sulphur mines and also in combination with other elements in certain minerals: they can occur as selenides and tellurides, as might be expected. The last and heaviest member of this group is polonium. Like other very heavy elements it is radioactive, that is, its atoms "decay" and turn into radio-lead. It was discovered by Mme Curie in pitchblende.

Five more substances to fall into a group are nitrogen, phosphorus, arsenic, antimony and bismuth. Nitrogen, the lightest of these, is a gas. Combined with oxygen it forms nitrates and with other elements it forms nitrites. Combined with hydrogen it forms ammonia. In biological tissues it is the essential element in protein. Phosphorus, which is heavier than nitrogen, is a reactive metal in its pure form. Combined with oxygen it yields phosphates and, in analogy with nitrogen, combined with hydrogen it forms phosphine. But whereas the smell of ammonia though strong is not unpleasant, that of phosphine is like rotten fish. Phosphorus, like nitrogen, is an essential element in living tissues. Its function is in the biological release of energy. Arsenic possesses chemical properties similar to those of other members of its group. Its heavier atom does not fit in properly with many biological systems but, because its chemistry allows it to fit in to some degree, its incompetent attempts (as it were) make it very poisonous. Antimony is a heavier and more stable metal than phosphorus—there is extant a Chaldean vase of 3000 B.C. made of pure antimony. In smelting its ores, antimony dioxide and antimony trioxide may be formed in the same way as oxides of arsenic or phosphorus (or nitrogen) occur. Similarly a gas, stibine, with a disagreeable smell is produced when antimony combines with hydrogen. Bismuth, the heaviest member of this group, is a brittle metal heavier than lead. It is used with lead as a component of Wood's metal because it possesses the property of making alloys easier to melt. Like other members of its group it forms oxides. It also forms a gaseous compound with hydrogen but this is unstable.

Although in trying to see what the science of chemistry is all about, we must obviously consider—as we are doing in this chapter—the different substances of which the things we find on earth are made, we can do better than simply try to reel off a catalogue of the whole ninety-two of them. Firstly, the remarkable similarities running through the elements that fall into the groups we have been discussing can today be explained, as we shall see in due course, by the modern theory of atomic structure. And secondly, this new understanding of the nature of atoms elucidates a good deal of the reason for the differences between the groups of elements. But there are one or two more of these groups that we still need to review in some detail because of the special interest of certain of their members. Of these, the most remarkable is the "carbon group".

Carbon has to be related to silicon, germanium, tin and lead. It is unique among the elements because of the quite remarkable facility it possesses of combining, not only with other substances, but with itself. It is capable of forming stable chains containing two or three carbon atoms only, or fifty or sixty atoms. These chains may be simple, like skipping ropes, or branched; crinkled up into springy coils or cross-linked like crochet mats. Because of this unique ability, fully half of all chemistry deals with carbon. The formal definition of "organic chemistry" is, in fact, "the chemistry of carbon compounds." This branch of chemistry includes all of biochemistry, the chemistry of coal, of petroleum, of textiles and of plastics.

So outstanding is carbon as an element, that it is perhaps odd to find that the other members of its group, though important in many respects are not strikingly more so than many other substances. Next heaviest to carbon is silicon. This is, second to oxygen, the most widely distributed substance of all. Just as carbon readily forms carbon dioxide, so silicon readily becomes silicon dioxide, which is quartz, sand or flint. Crystalline silicon has the same structure as diamond, that is, crystalline carbon. Again like carbon, silicon can form simple chain compounds. Silicon is the principal component of glass. As would be expected from its relationship with carbon, it is present in many plants and in the tissues and skeletons of certain animals. There are beds of diatomaceous earth in California more than a thousand feet thick and extending over several square miles, entirely composed of silicon dioxide collected in the bodies of once living diatoms (Fig. 15). Germanium is much less common than silicon. It is found in some zinc ores and in the ash of certain types of coal. Like silicon, its lighter group-mate, and tin, its next heavier, it combines with organic carbon radicles to form such compounds as tetra-ethyl derivatives and germano-chloroform. Germanium can also be introduced in place of silicon into crown glass to change the refractive index. Tin, heavier again than germanium, is a familiar metal. Its most obvious chemical similarities with carbon are that it combines with hydrogen as well as with oxygen. It also forms, in common with silicon and germanium, a long series of organo-metallic compounds with chains of tin atoms. Its similarity to germanium, below it in weight, and lead, above it, as a malleable metal is even more readily apparent. Lead also is familiar to the non-chemist. It is widely distributed in many parts of the world. It also forms organic compounds of which tetra-ethyl lead is probably the best known.

Following the "carbon group," we can perhaps slip rather quickly on to mention a group comprising boron, aluminium, gallium, indium and thallium; another made up of zinc, cadmium and mercury; the next including copper, silver and gold; then a group of nickel, palladium and platinum; followed by cobalt, rhodium and iridium; iron, ruthenium and osmium; manganese, technecium and rhenium; and then chromium, molybdenum, tungsten and uranium. Six artificial radioactive elements, californium, berkelium, curium, americum, pluto-

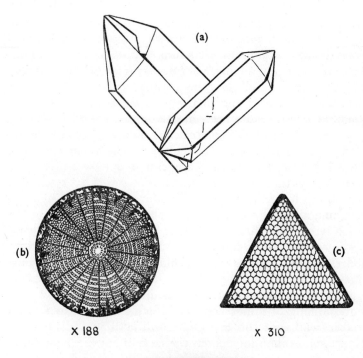

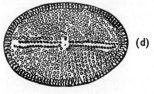

FIG. 15. Quartz and diatoms

(a) Quartz. (b) *Arachnoidiscus chenberghii*. (c) *Cathenesis splendida.*
(d) *Triceratium favas*

nium and neptunium, form a somewhat special group to themselves.

Having gone so far it is, perhaps, worth while itemising the remaining five groups to complete the list of all the known elements. Then we can discuss the quite remarkable modern discoveries that have turned them from a miscellaneous and unwieldy catalogue into an explicable and orderly sequence of substances. And so there are vanadium, niobium, tantalum and protactinium; titanium, zirconium, hafnium and thorium; scandium, yttrium, a cluster of fifteen so-called "rare earths," and actinium; beryllium, magnesium, calcium, strontium, barium and radium; and finally lithium, sodium, potassium, rubidium, caesium and francium.

Now many of the elements that we have just discussed and listed have been known by alchemists and the chemists who succeeded them for a long time. But it is only within very recent years that we have really grasped their systematic relationship to one another and thus moved quite away from the frame of mind when we should have had to believe that the existence and behaviour of different elements in the universe was purely random. Since these ideas are fundamental to modern chemistry, it is worth while discussing them in some detail.

The first step towards our modern and comparatively orderly understanding of things was due to John Dalton, an English Quaker, who wrote his first paper on the subject in 1803. He made three assumptions about the facts of chemical combinations. Firstly, he postulated that every chemical element was entirely made up of its own particular kind of atom different from any other, and all the atoms of any one element were identical, especially in weight. On the other hand, atoms of different elements have different properties and in particular they have different weights. Secondly, chemical compounds were entirely made up of identical particles, now called "molecules," each composed of a fixed and invariable number of atoms of the separate kinds of elements making up the compound. If this were true it meant that a particular compound always contained the same proportion of the component elements, and if there existed two compounds of the same elements, the quantities of one of these elements that combined with a given quantity of the other would be present in the proportion of whole numbers. Dalton showed by experiment that this was true. A third assumption arising from the others was that a chemical reaction consists in a redistribution of atoms so that the original molecules are broken up and new ones formed, containing all together the same number of the same kinds of atom. In the process none of the original atoms are destroyed and no new ones are created.

These principles, at the time they were stated, fitted the facts of chemistry as they were known very well and were quickly adopted into the fabric of science. In using his postulates, Dalton established the modern system of chemical formulae and chemical equations to explain what was happening in chemical reactions. Another fruitful offshoot of Dalton's thinking was the determination of the "atomic weights" of the various elements. This was done by comparing the relative weights of the separate elements in a number of compounds. For example water, which is composed of hydrogen and oxygen, always contains eight times the weight of oxygen to that of hydrogen. The present system of computing atomic weights is based on the use of oxygen as the base line with a conventional atomic weight of 16. By experiment and measurement from a variety of compounds of oxygen and hydrogen, it has been determined that the atomic weight of hydrogen is 1·008 compared with oxygen's 16.

The atomic weights of all the elements have been determined. The way this is usually done is to convert an exactly weighed amount of the element in question into a series of compounds with one or more different elements whose atomic weights are known. The atomic weights of the elements range from 1·008 for hydrogen by steps of two or three up to 16 for oxygen and thence up to californium, the heaviest element in the terrestrial world, with an atomic weight of 244.

Fifty or sixty years after Dalton first developed his atomic theory for chemistry, people began to consider some of the new facts emerging from the collection of information about atomic weights. In 1864, Newlands drew attention to a curious point. When elements were listed in order of their atomic weights it was found that substances with similar properties

TABLE I.—THE CHEMICAL ELEMENTS

Chemical symbol	Element	Atomic number	Atomic weight	Chemical symbol	Element	Atomic number	Atomic weight
A	Argon	18	39·944	Mn	Manganese	25	54·93
Ac	Actinium	89	227	Mo	Molybdenum	42	95·95
Ag	Silver	47	107·880	N	Nitrogen	7	14·008
Al	Aluminium	13	26·97	Na	Sodium	11	22·997
Am	Americium	95	—	Nb	Niobium (see Cb)	41	92·91
As	Arsenic	33	74·91	Nd	Neodymium	60	144·27
At	Astatine	85	—	Ne	Neon	10	20·183
Au	Gold	79	197·2	Ni	Nickel	28	58·69
B	Boron	5	10·82	Np	Neptunium	93	—
Ba	Barium	56	137·36	O	Oxygen	8	16·0000
Be	Beryllium	4	9·013	Os	Osmium	76	190·2
Bi	Bismuth	83	209·00	P	Phosphorus	15	30·98
Bk	Berkelium	97	—	Pa	Protactinium	91	231
Br	Bromine	35	79·916	Pb	Lead	82	207·21
C	Carbon	6	12·010	Pd	Palladium	46	106·7
Ca	Calcium	20	40·08	Pu	Plutonium	94	—
Cb	Columbium (see Nb)	41	92·91	Pm	Prometheum	61	—
Cd	Cadmium	48	112·41	Po	Polonium	84	210
Ce	Cerium	58	140·13	Pr	Praseodymium	59	140·92
Cf	Californium	98	—	Pt	Platinum	78	195·23
Cl	Chlorine	17	35·457	Ra	Radium	88	226·05
Cm	Curium	96	—	Rb	Rubidium	37	85·48
Co	Cobalt	27	58·94	Re	Rhenium	75	186·31

Symbol	Name	At. wt.	No.	Symbol	Name	At. wt.	No.
Cp	Cassiopeium (see Lu)	174·99	71	Rh	Rhodium	102·91	45
Cr	Chromium	52·01	24	Rn	Radon	222	86
Cs	Cesium	132·91	55	Ru	Ruthenium	101·7	44
Cu	Copper	63·57	29	S	Sulphur	32·066	16
Dy	Dysprosium	162·46	66	Sb	Antimony	121·76	51
Er	Erbium	167·2	68	Sc	Scandium	45·10	21
Eu	Europium	152·2	63	Se	Selenium	78·96	34
F	Fluorine	19·00	9	Si	Silicon	28·06	14
Fe	Iron	55·85	26	Sm	Samarium	150·43	62
Fr	Francium	—	87	Sn	Tin	118·70	50
Ga	Gallium	69·72	31	Sr	Strontium	87·63	38
Gd	Gadolinium	156·9	64	Ta	Tantalum	180·88	73
Ge	Germanium	72·60	32	Tb	Terbium	159·2	65
H	Hydrogen	1·0080	1	Tc	Technecium (see Ma)	—	43
He	Helium	4·003	2	Te	Tellurium	127·61	52
Hf	Hafnium	178·6	72	Th	Thorium	232·12	90
Hg	Mercury	200·61	80	Ti	Titanium	47·90	22
Ho	Holmium	164·94	67	Tl	Thallium	204·39	81
I	Iodine	126·92	53	Tm	Thulium	169·4	69
In	Indium	114·76	49	U	Uranium	238·07	92
Ir	Iridium	193·1	77	V	Vanadium	50·95	23
K	Potassium	39·096	19	W	Wolfram (Tungsten)	183·92	74
Kr	Krypton	83·7	36	Xe	Xenon	131·3	54
La	Lanthanum	138·92	57	Y	Yttrium	88·92	39
Li	Lithium	6·940	3	Yt	Ytterbium	173·04	70
Lu	Lutecium (see Cp)	174·99	71	Zn	Zinc	65·38	30
Ma	Massurium (see Tc)	—	43	Zr	Zirconium	91·22	40
Mg	Magnesium	24·32	12				

appeared in the list at regular intervals. A few years later, a Russian chemist, Mendeléev, pointed out that in a number of cases elements with similar characteristics turned up after each seventeen substances listed in order of their atomic weights. And when a similar element did not occur in seventeenth place, he prophesied (this was in 1869) that an unknown element would be discovered to fit into a vacant space to maintain the sequence of 17s. On several occasions he was later shown to be right. This regular sequence of the elements he called the "periodic table."

Since Mendeléev's time much more has been discovered about the chemical elements and a number of new ones have been found. There are, in fact, eighteen groups, not seventeen. The full "periodic table" is shown in Table II.

The exciting thing for the modern twentieth-century chemist is that there is now known to be a reason why these groups of elements, set out vertically in the table, should be similar in their characteristics, while at the same time most of them are arranged—as one might imagine arbitrarily—in order of their atomic weights. The atomic weights are listed beside each element's name in Table I. They go up, as can be seen, rather irregularly. Beside each element in Table II is what is called its "atomic number." This is derived from some rather complex modern physics that I shall not try to describe here. In brief, when a substance is heated until it is incandescent and the light it emits is looked at through a spectroscope, a number of lines can be seen at various places on the light spectrum. Every one of the elements exhibits a different arrangement of lines. Study of these line-spectrum patterns, and others like them produced by X-rays, enables physicists to estimate how many electron particles there are circling round the atomic nucleus in each type of atom. The number of these electrons is the "atomic number." This "atomic number" runs, as can be seen from Table I, from 1 for hydrogen up to 98 for californium in the same order with very few exceptions as the increasing atomic weights.

The atoms comprising the essential substance of each different element are, it now appears, all composed of the same

TABLE II.—THE PERIODIC SYSTEM OF THE ELEMENTS

														[$_1$H]				$_2$He
$_3$Li		$_4$Be		$_5$B				$_6$C		$_7$N		$_8$O		$_9$F				$_{10}$Ne
$_{11}$Na		$_{12}$Mg		$_{13}$Al				$_{14}$Si		$_{15}$P		$_{16}$S		$_{17}$Cl				$_{18}$A
$_{19}$K		$_{20}$Ca		$_{21}$Sc			$_{22}$Ti		$_{23}$V		$_{24}$Cr		$_{25}$Mn		$_{26}$Fe	$_{27}$Co	$_{28}$Ni	
	$_{29}$Cu		$_{30}$Zn	$_{31}$Ga				$_{32}$Ge		$_{33}$As		$_{34}$Se		$_{35}$Br				$_{36}$Kr
$_{37}$Rb		$_{38}$Sr		$_{39}$Y			$_{40}$Zr		$_{41}$Cb		$_{42}$Mo		$_{43}$Tc		$_{44}$Ru	$_{45}$Rh	$_{46}$Pd	
	$_{47}$Ag		$_{48}$Cd	$_{49}$In				$_{50}$Sn		$_{51}$Sb		$_{52}$Te		$_{53}$I				$_{54}$Xe
$_{55}$Cs		$_{56}$Ea		$_{57}$La	$_{58}$Ce	$_{59}$Pr		$_{60}$Nd		$_{61}$Pm		$_{62}$Sm	$_{63}$Eu	$_{64}$Gd	$_{65}$Tb		$_{66}$Dy	
$_{67}$Ho	$_{68}$Ev	$_{69}$Tm	$_{70}$Yb	$_{71}$Lu			$_{72}$Hf		$_{73}$Ta		$_{74}$W		$_{75}$Re		$_{76}$Os	$_{77}$Ir	$_{78}$Pt	
	$_{79}$Au		$_{80}$Hg	$_{81}$Tl				$_{82}$Pb		$_{83}$Bi		$_{84}$Po		$_{85}$At				$_{86}$Rn
$_{87}$Fr		$_{88}$Ra		$_{89}$Ac			$_{90}$Th		$_{91}$Pa		$_{92}$U		$_{93}$Np		$_{94}$Pu	$_{95}$Am	$_{96}$Cm	
$_{97}$Bk		$_{98}$Cf																

NOTE: The elements contained within the bold outline are known as "the Rare Earths".

material: a central heavy nucleus with series of small, active electrons spinning round and round it. The chemical difference between different elements is due to the fact that there are different numbers of electrons flying round each respective nucleus. (We shall discuss the differences in the nucleus later in this book.) The electrons are arranged in a series of "shells," one outside the other. Physical geometry decides that each "shell" can only hold so many electrons. If there are fewer than the number needed to fill a "shell," then the element concerned will be chemically reactive as electrons from outside fit themselves into spaces in the "shell." If the shell is complete, then the element will be chemically stable and unreactive. Each shell, working one's way outwards from the nucleus, tends to hold more electrons than the last, and as one gets to very heavy elements with a number of "shells" one outside the other, the atom itself becomes unstable and we get either naturally radioactive substances, like radium, or substances that can be caused to collapse, like uranium. Lastly, elements with the same number of unfilled vacancies in their electron shells tend to possess similar chemical properties—and this is the reason why, for example, carbon, silicon, germanium, tin and lead are all members of the same group. The look of their atomic structures is shown diagrammatically in Fig. 16.

The first "shell" holds two electrons. Hydrogen possesses only this "shell" and has only one electron in it. It is, therefore, a reactive substance. Helium has only this single "shell," but with its two electrons the shell is complete and it is, in consequence, an inert, unreactive element. Carbon, shown in Fig. 16, has three layers, the first holding two electrons, the second also holding two; but the third, capable of holding six, has only two in it. That is to say, there are four unfilled vacancies. Each of the other elements in the group, though possessing more and more layers of electron "layers," has four vacancies in the outermost. It is the existence of four unfilled electron-vacancies throughout the group that produces the similarity in the chemical properties of each substance.

The next group to that of carbon, namely nitrogen, phosphorus, arsenic, antimony and bismuth, have three vacancies in their outer electron shells, while the group on the other side, boron, aluminium, gallium, indium and thallium have five empty spaces. We shall discuss in more detail in the next chapter the practical effect of these differing atomic configurations on the chemical behaviour of individual substances. Meanwhile, there is a further important point to notice. When you

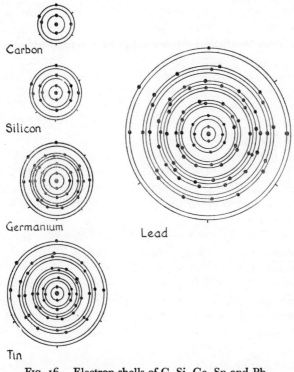

Carbon

Silicon

Germanium

Lead

Tin

FIG. 16.   Electron shells of C, Si, Ge, Sn and Pb

glance at Fig. 16, you can quickly see how the atomic structure of the increasingly heavy members of a group of elements becomes more and more complex and unwieldy. Lead, the heaviest member of the carbon group, contains six "shells" of electrons revolving round the nucleus of its atom, the first of one layer, two others made up of two layers, two of three layers, and one of four, that is fifteen layers altogether. If we had chosen another group of elements, for example, that made up of beryllium, magnesium, calcium, strontium, barium and radium, the diagrams of the first four substances would have looked like those illustrated in Fig. 16. The only difference would be that these all possess six electron-vacancies—that is to say the outer layer, capable of holding just six electrons, would be missing.

In the beryllium group the fifth substance, barium, is much lighter than lead, the corresponding substance of the carbon group. The conditions of pressure and temperature on this earth, however, allow another heavier substance beyond barium to exist in this group, namely radium. It possesses the customary inner "shell" of one layer of electrons, the second "shell" of two layers, the third of three, the fourth of four, the fifth of three, the sixth of two, but then over and above these there is a seventh "shell" of yet one more layer of electrons. This total of sixteen layers seems to make the strain of internal cohesion almost too much for the radium atom. Like a juggler keeping a cascade of tennis balls in the air all at once, the problem of controlling eighty-eight revolving electrons is well nigh overwhelming. In fact, the atom is, as is well known, unstable. Consequently, radium is radioactive. Indeed, all the heavy elements at the bottom of the Periodic Table with atomic numbers greater than 86 are similarly unstable.

Of course, this description of the make-up of the different elements on earth and their relationship to each other is in some respects an over-simplification. For instance, the electrons that circulate round and round the nucleus of each kind of atom, in larger and larger numbers as the atomic weights of the successive elements gets heavier and heavier, each carry a negative electrical charge. The force that keeps this cluster of electrons in place and prevents it from flying away by centrifugal force is a compensating positive electric charge contained in the nucleus of each atom. I do not propose to go into any detailed description of nuclear structure at this point. It would lead perhaps too far from chemistry, as it is generally understood, for the outset of this book. The exciting and interesting new understanding of chemistry, that has developed only during this present century, is that all the substances we know, whether they seem as different as the oxygen we breathe on the one hand and a lump of lead on the other, are in fact composed of the same stuff, namely electrons circling round a nucleus.

The modern chemist has emerged from the "descriptive phase" of his science, when all he could hope to do in trying to get an intellectual grasp of chemistry was to learn that one kind of element possessed this or that property, that another was heavy or light, or explosive or not, that a third went blue when you cooled it and white when it was hot. It is true that he must still learn all this information—or at least must know where to find it. Today, however, he can understand that his science does not deal with a miscellaneous collection of substances. He now knows that underlying the variations in the substances he sees around him in the everyday world, and behind the reactions and changes brought about in the laboratory, all the elements on earth are composed of the same basic material. The atoms of everything, in fact, comprise a nucleus surrounded by clusters of electrons ranging from 1 to 98 in number. And although the chemist cannot turn lead into gold, his colleague the physicist can—or at least understands the relationship between them. It is now possible to knock bits off the nucleus of an atom and thus to make another substance of lower atomic weight, or, on the other hand, by causing collisions to take place against the nucleus of an atom to add pieces on and thus make elements of higher atomic weight.

This is physics, as I have said, not chemistry. Chemical reactions, which we shall be discussing in the next chapter, depend on the electron shells circling round the nucleus of each different element, but—and this indeed is the crucial modern distinction—a basic assumption of chemical science is that chemical elements do not change their atomic structure throughout the course of all the chemical actions and reactions they undergo.

Before we move on to a consideration of the more practical achievements of chemistry, I should like to pause to include one further remarkable extension of the modern understanding of the nature of chemical substances.

There is good evidence from experiments in the laboratory
as well as from the observations of astrophysics that the elements have been and are still being synthesised in stars. Modern
physicists and mathematicians can now explain the relative
amounts of practically all the elements from the lightest, that is
hydrogen with an atomic weight of 1·008, up to and through
heavy elements such as uranium, with an atomic weight of 238,
as they are seen and identified by spectrographic and other
means in various types of stars. Hydrogen is, as we have seen,
the simplest atom with its single electron and simple heavy
nucleus. At temperatures of from 10 million up to 50 million
degrees centigrade that are known to exist in "main-sequence"
stars, atoms of hydrogen fuse together by a process now called
by astronomers "thermal cooking" to form helium. We know
something about this sort of thing on earth in our man-made
"hydrogen bombs." When the temperature in stars gets hotter,
up to, say, 100 million to 200 million degrees C.—which is the
temperature of red giant stars—helium atoms are transformed,
principally to carbon, oxygen and neon. Hotter still, that is up
to 1000 million degrees C., magnesium, silicon, sulphur, argon
and calcium are formed from the simpler carbon, oxygen and
neon. The synthesis of iron atoms takes place at even greater
temperatures of 2000 to 5000 million degrees C.

More complicated effects have been followed by physicists
when they observe the "thermal cooking," not of completely
pure hydrogen atoms, but of hydrogen mixed with small proportions of the carbon, oxygen, neon and iron that have already
been synthesised by, or ejected from, previously existing stars.
Such effects as the mixing of the core and the envelope in the
"giant stage" in the natural history of stars can now be com-
prehended to explain the variety of chemistry to be seen in the
heavens.

It would be inappropriate in a book such as this, designed to
explain what the chemistry we use in our present, daily, indus-
trialised, twentieth-century life is all about, to try to set out the
modern scientific views about the birth, growth, development
and ultimate decay of the stars. Nevertheless, when we start to
deal with the lead and tin, the copper, sulphur, chromium and

arsenic of everyday affairs, it is worth knowing that Dr Hoyle of Cambridge, Professor Fowler of the California Institute of Technology and their colleagues, turning from a discussion of the origin of the chemical elements in the stars to the substances we find on earth, wrote this in 1956 in a learned scientific paper:

If we suppose that the elements of which the earth is composed were not all built at one moment of time but were built at a uniform rate, starting at the time of origin of the galaxy and extending almost up to the formation of the solar system some 5000 million years ago, then using the ratio of uranium isotopes found at present in the earth, the age of the galaxy can be calculated.

We could take this to mean that the variety of chemicals with which we have to deal and their relative amounts one to another are dependent on the age of the little star round which we fly—I refer, of course, to the sun.

It is exciting and stimulating to know about the theoretical basis lying behind the existence of the chemical elements. Furthermore, our present understanding is of practical usefulness in assessing the similarities of the substances to be found in the eighteen separate groups of the Periodic Table. When we know that each similar substance has a similar arrangement of electrons in at least its outermost electron "shell," we possess a very practical clue to the best method of handling it.

At the beginning of the nineteenth century the dividing line between chemistry and physics was a blurred one. For example, it was a commonly held theory at that time that heat was a sort of matter. It was thought of as a cloud of tiny material particles that could penetrate through and into bodies. It had, in fact, been listed by Lavoisier as a chemical element called "caloric." But because a hot body weighed no more than a cold one, "caloric" had to be treated as weightless, a property that distinguished it from any other element. The prime difficulty about this theory was to explain the production of heat by friction. The general idea was that when two things got hot by being rubbed together, "caloric" was being squeezed out of them. Count Rumford carried out an experiment that made this theory appear ridiculous. He fixed a metal box on to a gun barrel that was being bored by a great machine turned by horses. The metal box was filled with water which soon got hot and began to boil. It could be refilled again and again. Since no chemical change could be demonstrated in the iron before or after the boring process, the notion that something was being wrung out of it had to be abandoned.

Present understanding is that heat is not a form of material substance, but a form of energy. When a man receives a punch on the nose, the thing that strikes him is a mixture of chemical compounds whereas the impact on his nose is energy. When a solid chemical substance, be it an iron bar or a block of ice, is gradually warmed, energy is put into it. The effect of the energy is to spin the electrons circulating round the atomic nuclei in a wider orbit. At a temperature characteristic of the particular substance in question the amount of molecular movement becomes such that the coherence of the substance as a solid breaks down and it becomes liquid. Chemically the substance has not changed. Liquid iron is still iron, and liquid water is H_2O just as is solid ice. If more energy is put into the system the molecular movement becomes so violent that the liquid cannot stay as such and it becomes a gas. Again, this is a physical change not a chemical one. These physical changes are reversible. When the temperature of a gas falls its molecules (oxygen, for example, does not exist as a cloud of separate oxygen atoms but as pairs of oxygen atoms, written O_2. Each unit of this natural compound, namely O_2, makes up a single molecule) fall together at a fixed temperature and pressure characteristic of the particular gas and become liquid. But when a substance is heated to such a temperature that it breaks down into something else or combines with its environment to form something new, this is a chemical change, and is recognisable as such because it may not be easily reversible and also because it involves measurable weights of substances about which chemical balance sheets can be drawn up.

Classical chemistry says that heat, electricity, light and motion are not *substances* but are different manifestations of *energy*. They cannot be weighed and measured, says the traditional textbook of chemistry upon which many of us have been brought up. For all immediately practical purposes this approach to chemistry is true and accurate enough. For example, a hot hot-water bottle does not weigh any more than a cold hot-water bottle. We define the difference between the two hot-water bottles as a physical one—the water molecules are merely vibrating more rapidly. On the other hand a slab of rusty iron does weigh more than the same slab shining. The rustiness, that is the oxidation of the iron, is a chemical change.

In the next chapter we are, as I have said, going to discuss the nature of the chemical changes and reactions that are made use of in all the practical things that chemistry does today. Meanwhile, however, it is worth while pausing to consider that although today the textbooks can be dogmatic about what distinguishes a chemical change from a physical one, the rate at which the underlying theories of the physical nature of the world is altering may in the quite near future cause the chemist to revise his views. As I have said, the weightless element is officially unacceptable to chemistry. Heat, electricity and movement are, so chemistry has said up to now, not chemical elements but merely different forms of energy. This is still true for the useful workaday chemists who have to make our steel and our dyes and our nylon stockings. But it is not quite true to the physicists who dig deeper into the chemical "subconscious," as it were. It is reasonable to draw a line between atomic physics and classical chemistry as it has been generally accepted and I shall do so from now on. These are two aspects of science. But nevertheless ever since Einstein at the beginning of the century demonstrated that mass (that is a weight of "solid" stuff) and energy were interrelated every chemist has been aware that behind his perfectly clearly understood operations there is a further layer, as it were, of physical structure and reaction.

3

Chemical Reactions

Information about an immense diversity of chemical reactions has been collected since chemistry first began as a body of practical experience in Egypt, later to be systematised in the Arabia of the seventh century. Today when we talk about chemical action we mean the production of something so completely altered as to be legitimately considered as a new substance with properties recognisably different from those of the components from which it was formed. Rust, for example, is quite different from the invisible gas, oxygen, and the iron railings from which it is derived. The modern chemist, possessing the knowledge we have been discussing in the last chapter, attributes the properties of every substance to the chemical components of its molecules, that is to say, to the nature of the atoms which are present in each molecule of the particular substance, and to the manner of their arrangement. Thus, salt is different from baking powder because the molecules of salt are made up of atoms of sodium and chlorine whereas those of baking powder comprise sodium combined with carbon, oxygen and hydrogen (Fig. 17). On the other hand, alcohol is quite different from dimethyl ether although both possess molecules containing identical atoms in identical proportions —both in fact possess the formula C_2H_6O—but in this instance the atoms in the two molecules are differently arranged.

Salt

Baking Soda

FIG. 17.   Crystals of salt and baking soda

The complete change of properties which is brought about by chemical action is due to the recombination or rearrangement of atoms to produce new sorts of molecules. It is the business of chemistry to bring about chemical changes and to control and manage them while they are going on. When two or more kinds of atom combine together they do so because their outer shell of electrons possesses gaps that "mesh" into each other, as it were. The vigour—that is, the speed—with which chemical combinations and decompositions occur is due to the action of electrical forces, the nature of which is complex and is dependent again on the inner structure of the particular atoms. T.N.T. and dynamite detonate with great vigour, whereas the "combustion" of iron and its consequent conversion to rust may proceed slowly and continuously for centuries.

There are a number of other factors, besides the different nature of each separate chemical molecule, that effect the rate at which chemical changes occur. For example, the relative amounts of the different reacting substances often has a good deal to do with what happens. When two substances combine together to form a third, it sometimes happens that the action starts quite vigorously and then gradually slows down as the amount of the two original substances becomes less and less and the concentration of the newly formed substance more and more. If the chemist in charge of the process collects the third compound continuously while it is being produced, the reaction can often be made to proceed until all the starting substances are used up. The "law of mass action" as it is called, says that the tendency of a chemical reaction to go in one particular direction—that is, for our two starting materials to react to form the third—is opposed by a tendency for the substances produced to react the other way—that is, for the third compound, in our example, to turn itself back into the other two. And the more there are of the substances on one side of the operation, the stronger is their influence on which direction the reaction goes. As originally defined by the Norwegians who elucidated it in 1864, the mass-action law was that the "chemical action of a substance at any moment was proportional to its active amount at that time."

Three other factors which influence the progress of chemical changes must be mentioned. The first is heat. As a general rule an increase in temperature increases the rate at which a chemical reaction takes place. Some changes, like the dissolution of a strip of copper in dilute sulphuric acid, with the formation of the blue substance, copper sulphate, take place under cold conditions but go faster when the temperature becomes hotter. Other reactions, like the chemical combination of the carbon in a wooden match with the oxygen of the atmosphere require the attainment of quite a high temperature—in this case about 700° C. before they start at all. The sign of chemical activity for the match is that it bursts into flames.

A second factor influencing the speed of chemical processes is the presence or absence of a particular substance which may increase or diminish this speed without itself taking any part in the process. The substance that does this is called a "catalyst." Catalysts are of the highest importance in chemical practice and we shall refer to them many times. It is a humbling thought that although an immense amount is known about the practice and theory of chemistry and can be found in textbooks, research papers and monographs without number, science has not yet progressed to the point where it is possible to predict what substance can be used as a catalyst for any particular chemical operation. And yet the great tonnages of ammonium salts obtained by nitrogen fixation from the atmosphere depend on the use of catalysts. The up-to-date petroleum engineer also uses catalysts to work his "cat-cracker" to produce chemicals from crude oil. A simple example of a catalyst is the moisture that enables oxygen to combine with iron in the formation of rust. The damp that "causes" rusting does not itself take part in the chemical reaction although without it the reaction may not occur at all.

The third factor that has a practical influence on how a chemical reaction proceeds is the supply of energy to it from an outside source. We have already referred to heat. But light also affects chemical reactions. Indeed, the substantial branch of chemistry represented by the photographic industry in all its ramifications depends on this effect. Electricity is also a source of energy that, as can readily be appreciated from our discussion of the fundamentally electrical nature of matter itself, exerts an influence. Electrolysis, well known in the industrial operation of electroplating, is an example.

These then are the factors that influence the rate and character of chemical change: the supply of outside energy, the presence of a catalyst, the temperature at which the reaction takes place, the amounts of the different substances taking part, and—most significant of all—the nature of the molecules involved. It is obviously impossible in a book of this sort to attempt to describe all there is to know about the infinity of chemical substances that can be involved in reactions with each other. It is interesting to note, however, that the enormous growth in chemical industry that has occurred during recent years has to a remarkable degree paralleled a fresh and simplified approach to the complexities of chemical science.

British chemical industry has been in existence in something like its present form for about a hundred years. Britain, and indeed Europe as a whole, had a large and prosperous chemical industry long before the United States, and in its development Germany played a leading part. The industry was built up by collaboration between chemists who worked out in their laboratories ways of making useful substances and engineers who designed and built the production plants. In general, the plants they designed were scaled-up versions of the chemist's bench apparatus, and they committed the industry to batch processes in which the addition of the different ingredients, the carrying out of the appropriate operations and the removal of products are a sequence of separate steps. This batch system imposed limits on the size of the operation and became more and more unwieldy as the chemical processes became increasingly complex.

American chemical manufacturers, coming on the scene some fifty years ago, looked with fresh eyes on what was involved in this use of chemistry in manufacture. They quickly realised that chemistry, though complex in its details and varied in its use of more or fewer of the ninety-two elements and their innumerable combinations, was simple in its principles. The solution to the problem had, in fact, been suggested by

George Davis in a series of lectures given in the Manchester Technical School in 1887, but it was not until about 1914 that the clear thinking of A. D. Little and his colleagues at the Massachusetts Institute of Technology developed the concept of "unit processes" in large-scale chemical operations. The fundamental principle of this idea, that can be applied equally well to the description of chemical science as to the design of chemical factories, is that all processes of chemical manufacture can be broken down into a series of basic operations. The physical operations are the flow of fluids, the transmission of heat, evaporation, distillation, the absorption of gases, solvent extraction, drying or humidifying, the separation of solids from liquids, grinding, mixing and so on. Chemical operations can be split up into such subdivisions as combustion, oxidation, neutralisation, nitration, condensation and other similar "unit processes" each of which can be studied and controlled. This conception of "unit operations" is, in the field of chemical industry, what the splitting up of manufacturing processes, so dramatically applied by Henry Ford, is to the mechanical industry. It is the men who were trained in the American technological colleges in this new concept as "chemical engineers" who have been responsible for the enormous development of chemistry and chemical manufacture in the United States between 1920 and the present day.

An examination of some of the more important "unit processes" of chemical engineering gives us at the same time illustrations of the main chemical "laws" and also an illustration of how these reactions are brought about and used.

Combustion

Combustion denotes the process of burning in the sense that a combustible substance is consumed by fire and flames. This simple definition contains at least three important principles of chemical science. The first is that of *the nature of fire itself*. For a very long time, from the classical ages right up to the end of the eighteenth century, fire was considered to be an actual material contained within the chemical elements. It is now clearly understood to be the release of energy occurring when oxygen combines with whatever is being burned. The conception of oxidation, that is this combination with oxygen, is basic to much of chemistry. We live in a world surrounded by an atmosphere in which oxygen is the active agent.

Oxygen, as we saw in the last chapter, possesses in its atomic structure two "vacant slots", as it were, in its outer electron shell. This enables it to combine with a large number of the other elements of the earth. The most important of these are hydrogen and carbon, both of which are also widely distributed. Most examples of combustion involve the chemical combination of carbon with oxygen. All sorts of other elements can, however, be oxidised. Iron when it rusts becomes iron oxide. Calcium never exists naturally as such, but its oxidised form, namely calcium oxide, is quicklime and this in turn when left to itself becomes calcium hydroxide, or calcium carbonate—a stable and permanent substance, limestone.

This brings us to a second important chemical principle inherent in the conception of combustion: I am referring to *energy*. Heat, explosion, electricity—all are different expressions of energy. When energy in the form of heat is applied to steam, the steam expands and makes a locomotive go, and part of the heat is recovered as movement. Similarly, electricity pushing through the "element" of an electric fire makes it hot and we recover part of the electrical energy as heat. We have already referred to Rumford's experimental demonstration of the equivalence between mechanical work and heat. Chemical energy fits into this same picture.

All of us who have sat in front of a fire know very well that the combustion of coal, which in simplified chemical terms is the oxidation of the carbon in the coal to CO_2 and the hydrogen in it to H_2O, gives off heat. The explanation is reasoned out like this.

Two grammes of hydrogen always combine with 16 grammes of oxygen. Now this amount of hydrogen (when it is in its basic form of gas) occupies 22·4 litres, that is about 5 gallons, and the oxygen occupies about $2\frac{1}{2}$ gallons. The volume of the two, therefore, is some $7\frac{1}{2}$ gallons. If one puts a match to the mixture, combustion takes place and the volume of gases collapses to nothing. Not quite nothing, though, because 18 ml., or about a dessertspoonful, of water is produced. But when the collapse occurs, the amount of energy needed by the oxygen and the hydrogen to sustain their previous volumes against the pressure of the atmosphere is released and appears as heat. The energy needed to sustain the gas volume as well as the amount of heat produced, can be measured in the laboratory and are found to tally. In fact, therefore, chemical energy or heat is the same sort of thing as other kinds of energy and can be reckoned in the same kind of way.

This is not the place to go into details of the mathematical calculations needed to reckon up the energy needed to support the 7½-gallon gas volume which when released produces the heat of combustion of hydrogen and oxygen. The answer to the sum is that 68 kilo-calories of heat are released in the formation of one gramme-molecule of water from this volume of oxygen and hydrogen. Similarly, 94 kilo-calories of heat are produced when carbon is combusted with oxygen to produce a gramme-molecule of carbon dioxide. This is the energy given out by the common forms of combustion with which we are familiar in the sitting-room fireplace.

In chemical terms, the release of heat in a fire—combustion, that is—is an example of an "exothermic reaction." There are a large number of other "exothermic reactions". For example, sulphur burns in oxygen to form sulphur dioxide and the release of 71 kilo-calories per gramme-molecule. But the combination of oxygen with another element is not an essential for the release of chemical energy. Iron combines with chlorine, to name one reaction in many, to produce iron chloride with the release of 96 kilo-calories per gramme-molecule. There is, however, a basic principle about energy-releasing reactions. It is this.

One of Newton's "laws," as they are called, enshrines in scientific terms a fundamental piece of common sense. The law says "an isolated system tends to an entropy." This means that unless you wind up your watch, it will sooner or later run down. Or, unless you blow up a balloon, it will eventually collapse. In chemical terms, "reduced" carbon (that is to say carbon that has not been oxidised) and oxygen are, as it were, blown-up balloons. When we put a match to the fire the balloon is pricked and energy is released—as heat in a fireplace or as work in a steam engine. The fundamental point is that when you get chemical energy, whether it is by way of combustion or by any other reaction, you can only get what is already there. Combustion demands the presence of fuel and this fuel, be it coal or petroleum or some less common substance, usually ends up as CO_2. You can get back again from CO_2, the already oxidised form of carbon, to a reduced (and consequently combustible) form of carbon if you put back the energy. In this earth, the energy is usually derived from sunshine and is channelled in by green plants, which are, of course, the original source of the coal.

The third chemical principle that arises from the apparently simple process of combustion is that *it does not necessarily occur all at once*. Most motorists will have had an inkling of this fact when the engine of their car "knocks." Combustion occurs as a wave of chemical reaction running from molecule to molecule through the entire volume. "Knocking" occurs when the conditions of pressure and temperature in the engine cylinder are such that the wave of combustion does not syncronise with the movement of the piston. A further point is that when, as may often happen, the chemistry of combustion does not go to completion in one step, the heat or energy produced in each intermediate step when added up always comes to the same total as would have been released had the reaction occurred as one operation. For example, carbon completely oxidised becomes CO_2, that is carbon dioxide. Partly oxidised it becomes CO, carbon monoxide. This is produced in a night watchman's brazier, also in the town gas-works. And the heat produced by combusting carbon to carbon dioxide, is the same as that produced when carbon is first oxidised to carbon monoxide and then subsequantly (in the family gas stove) from carbon monoxide to carbon dioxide.

We shall refer again to the chemical reaction of combustion in its practical context when we discuss smelting in Chapter 4 and the chemistry of coal and its products in Chapter 8.

Oxidation and Reduction

Oxidation and its converse *reduction* are reactions that are of general importance throughout the science of chemistry. Before we can apprehend the basis of oxidation and reduction, it is first necessary to grasp the conception of an element as we see and feel it—the metal copper, for example,—and its "ion," namely the electrically charged *"cupric ion,"* Cu^{++}, or the less highly charged *"cuprous ion,"* Cu^+. These "ions" do not "exist," in the ordinary sense, on their own but are the forms of copper which take part in chemical reactions as I shall now try to explain.

To take an example of chemical combinations, sodium combines with chlorine to form sodium chloride, which is common salt, because the outer electron shell of the chlorine atom, containing seven electrons, possesses the power under appropriate circumstances of "sucking in," as it were, the single electron circulating in the outer shell of the sodium atom. Salt is a stable substance because the two atoms of which it is composed link together to share the new combined 8-electron shell. Fig. 18 is the diagram of sodium chloride.

Now chlorine, when it exists in its elementary form as a gas, does not possess any electrical charge. The chloride ion in combination with another element has, however, drawn in an electron, as is shown in the diagram. An electron is defined by the physicists as a unit or corpuscle of negative electricity. It is this quite large amount of electricity that changes the properties of chlorine. For example, the negatively charged chloride ion, as it now is, is freed when salt, sodium chloride, is dissolved in water, and it is then capable of combining with some other appropriate ion, if one happens to be available. On the other hand, sodium, which is a soft, shining metal in its elemental form, becomes positively charged when it loses an electron (as it does when it combines with chlorine). The sodium ion, that is a sodium atom with a preponderance of positive electric charge due to its loss of a negative electron, is different in its properties from sodium element, just as chloride ion is different from chlorine.

It is the complex laws of electronic theory that decide which of the atoms are to lose electrons in chemical combinations and which are to gain them. Those that draw electrons towards themselves and consequently become negatively charged are called *anions*, whereas those that lose electrons and become positively charged are called *cations*. Some elements exhibit more pronounced electrochemical properties than others. Metals such as iron, copper, mercury, sodium, potassium and many more are strongly "polar" in their behaviour and readily lose electrons (consequently becoming positively charged) in forming the ions which take part in chemical combinations.

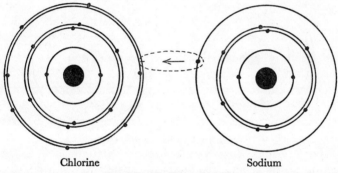

Chlorine   Sodium
FIG. 18.   Sodium chloride

The so-called "halogen" elements—fluorine, chlorine, iodine and bromine—and certain groups of elements that tend to act together as if they were one (technically known as "radicals"), for example, carbonate $CO_3^=$, sulphate $SO_4^=$, nitrate NO_3^- and so on, are on the other hand quite vigorous in their absorption of electrons and thus acquisition of negative charges when they exist in ionic form. When these polar ions combine, the linkage between them is described as *electrovalency*. When, as in sodium chloride illustrated in Fig. 18, only one electron is concerned in the linkage, the substance involved is said to possess a *valency* of 1, or to be monovalent. Sodium, that is, is monovalent. Calcium, on the other hand, possesses two electrons in its outer shell that it is prepared, quite vigorously, to transfer in its ionised state. It is, therefore, divalent—that is, it possesses a valency of 2. Consequently, since the chloride ion as we have seen can only fit one electron into its outer shell of seven, it takes two chloride ions to make a stable compound with calcium. The formula for calcium chloride is, therefore, $CaCl_2$.

Much of chemical combination depends on *electrovalency*, in which an electron, or several electrons, are drawn across from the element acting as cation to the element forming the anion. There is another form of linkage, however, called *co-valency*. This involves the sharing of two electrons. Chlorine gas, for

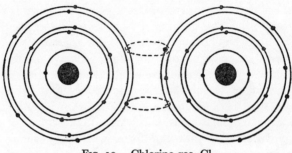

FIG. 19.   Chlorine gas, Cl_2

example, exists as Cl_2. The diagram of this 2-atom molecule is shown in Fig. 19.

The concepts of *valency*, and of positively charged *cations* and negatively charged *anions*, are all needed to describe the basic principle of the idea of *oxidation* and *reduction*, which is what we set out to talk about. The fundamental discovery of Lavoisier in 1796 was that the combustion of carbon-containing substances was the chemical combination of the carbon with oxygen. It was, in fact, an example of oxidation. Its great importance was that this reaction releases energy. Lavoisier also discovered that the same reaction was taking place when carbon-containing food was utilised by the body. And here again energy and heat were released.

Now oxygen forms a negatively charged ion. It is, in fact, capable of fitting two negative charges, that is two electrons, into its outer valency shell of electrons. And the ultimate substance best capable of supplying the electrons is hydrogen, the element possessing one electron shell only, containing just one electron. Before the present understanding of the electron concept was available, the term "oxidation" was applied only to reactions in which an element gained oxygen, for example, the burning of carbon, $C + O_2 \longrightarrow CO_2$, or the rusting of iron, $4Fe + 3O_2 \longrightarrow 2Fe_2O_3$. At the same time the term "reduction", the converse of oxidation, designated a reaction by which an element lost oxygen. An example is the reduction of copper oxide by hydrogen thus: $CuO + H_2 \longrightarrow Cu + H_2O$. Nowadays, an element which loses electrons in the course of chemical change and thus acquires a positive charge is said to be *oxidised*, while one gaining an electron and consequently adding a negative charge is said to be *reduced*. When two "polar" substances react together, one is always oxidised and one reduced, because one or more electrons are drawn across from one element to the other. Some elements, of which iron is one, can exist in several forms with different valencies. Iron is a cationic element, that is, it is a potential electron-giver. It consequently follows that the form with the valency of 3 (capable of releasing three electrons from its outer shell) is described as more highly oxidised than iron with valency 2.

Neutralisation

Another basic "unit process" of chemistry that needs describing is *neutralisation*. This presupposes the existence of *acids*, and of their opposites, *bases*. Robert Boyle described in 1664 the properties that make one define a substance as an acid. (1) It has a sour taste, (2) it can act as a solvent of varying power (that is, some acids are stronger than others), (3) it is capable of turning certain blue vegetable pigments red and the red can be turned back to blue by an alkali, or base. Litmus is, of course, the best known of these vegetable pigments. Finally, (4) an acid reacts with an alkali to produce a neutral *salt*. The commonest so-called mineral acids are sulphuric, hydrochloric and nitric. The best known organic acid is acetic acid, which is the active ingredient in vinegar. *Alkalis*, or bases, are perhaps of even greater antiquity than acids. The properties that make an alkali are: (1) its solution feels slimy when rubbed between one's fingers, (2) it turns red litmus blue, and (3) it can neutralise an acid to produce a salt.

Chemists gradually got an idea of what they meant by an acid, some time before they were able to define in chemical terms what an acid was. Things, of course, were even more difficult with regard to "bases" or "alkalis," since they were, by definition, the chemical opposites of acids. There are today a number of modern theories, but the classical conception of Humphrey Davy in England, Gay-Lussac in France and then, in 1887, Arrhenius in Sweden is still substantially valid.

Acids may be solid under ordinary conditions, like tartaric acid, or they may be liquid like sulphuric acid, or gaseous like hydrochloric acid. But they can barely be said to exert their function as acids until they are dissolved in water. When this occurs they become *ionised*. And one of the ions that frees itself from the acid molecule is the hydrogen ion—that is a hydrogen atom that has given up an electron and is consequently charged with positive electricity. It is today quite clear that the "strength" of an acid is the measure of the concentration of hydrogen ions it produces when it is dissolved in water. This "strength" arises in two ways. Firstly, some acids split up in water into one basic (that is, alkaline) radical and one hydrogen ion per molecule, while other acids possess two or three available hydrogen ions. Examples are nitric acid and sulphuric acid:

$$HNO_3 \longrightarrow \quad H^+ + NO_3^-$$
Nitric acid 1 hydrogen ion + nitrate ion.

$$H_2SO_4 \longrightarrow \quad H^+ + H^+ + SO_4^=$$
Sulphuric acid 2 hydrogen ions + sulphate ion.

The other factor affecting the "strength" of an acid is the degree to which it becomes ionised when it is dissolved in water. The so-called mineral acids, sulphuric, nitric, hydrochloric and the rest, are almost completely ionised, that is, they split completely into ions as soon as they mingle with water. Other kinds of acids, however, for example the acetic acid in vinegar, are less strong because part of the original molecule remains un-ionised. There is, indeed, some tendency for the ions to recombine and for the original molecule itself to be reconstituted according to the "law of mass action" instead of being broken down. This implies that the full content of hydrogen ions (that make the acid an acid) are never fully deployed. For this reason, acetic acid is not as "strong" as, say, sulphuric or nitric acid. This tendency for ionisation to go backwards as well as forwards is usually written:

$$HOOC \cdot CH_3 \quad \rightleftharpoons \quad H^+ \quad + \quad OOC \cdot CH_3{}^-$$

| Acetic | Hydrogen | Acetate ion |
| acid | ion | |

Since acid properties, as now defined, are a measure of the concentration of hydrogen ions in a solution, it is no cause for surprise to find that the qualities that were traditionally known to make an alkali what it is—its "caustic" properties, its sliminess and, above all, its power to neutralise acids—are now recognised, in the light of modern chemical theory, to be due to its capacity to release *hydroxyl ions*, that is OH$^-$, when dissolved in water. A convenient method of recording acidity or alkalinity, which is now very widely used in chemistry, is that invented in 1909 by S. P. L. Sörensen. It is the so-called *pH measurement*. In fact, the pH value expressed as a numeral is a measure of the hydrogen ion concentration of a solution. The figure used is the *negative logarithm*. This means that the larger the figure the lower is the concentration of hydrogen ions.

Water is (almost by definition) neutral: that is, it is neither acid nor alkaline. The ions in water, H_2O, are, of course, hydrogen ions H$^+$ and hydroxyl ions OH$^-$; and, because water is neutral, they are present in equal concentrations. Expressed in the Sörensen notation, the pH of water is 7·0. When a solution becomes acid and the concentration of hydrogen ions increases, the pH value falls, and the number becomes smaller and smaller as the acid grows stronger and stronger. On the other hand, when the concentration of hydrogen ions in any solution is smaller than the concentration of hydroxyl ions, that solution is alkaline and the pH value is larger than 7·0 (Fig. 20).

The degree of acidity or alkalinity affects the progress of a great many kinds of chemical reaction. Acids are used in petroleum refining, in "pickling" steel, in the manufacture of plastics, solvents and much else. In biology, the balance between the acidity and the alkalinity of living tissues is crucial to life. In our own bodies, the pH of the liquid fraction of the blood stream is maintained with great precision at 7·35, that is, just slightly alkaline. If this value changes by all but the smallest amount, life becomes impossible and we die.

FIG. 20.   A pH meter, direct reading

The common alkalis, caustic soda, caustic potash, sodium carbonate and ammonia, like the acids they oppose, are also used in many chemical operations. The manufacture of soap and of glass are two industrial uses of alkalis. But their basic significance is in balance with acids. As I set out to say a page or two back, neutralisation of acids by alkalis is a fundamental chemical "unit process."

Double decomposition

The fundamental chemical ideas of oxidation and reduction and of acids and alkalis are backed up by a number of lesser operations. For example, double decomposition takes place when two compounds react in such a way as to be converted into two others by "changing partners," as it were. Copper sulphate and sodium carbonate can react to produce copper carbonate and sodium sulphate.

Nitration

To achieve certain results, it is necessary to convert the substance used as starting material into its nitrate. The process is called *nitration*. This operation is done to glycerine in the manufacture of the explosive, nitroglycerine. It is necessary to know what one is doing to carry out the reaction successfully. The shorthand equation of what happens is as follows:

$$C_3H_5 \cdot (OH)_3 \quad + \quad 3NO_3 \cdot H \quad = \quad C_3H_5 \cdot (NO_3)_3 + 3H_2O$$

Glycerine   Nitric acid = Nitroglycerine   Water

To start with, the chemist who is treating glycerine with nitric acid keeps the reaction going forward or, if one likes to look at it differently, prevents it from going back, by taking the water that is formed out of circulation continuously as the process continues. This is done by having concentrated sulphuric acid present, since this acid possesses a strong affinity for water. But the rate of reaction, affected by the temperature and the amounts of the ingredients present, needs to be regulated with very great care because the oxygen atoms in the nitrate radical, NO_3^-, now attached to the carbon structure of the glycerine, possess a pronounced tendency to react with it to produce, among other end-products, CO_2—and to explode in doing so. For this reason, in industry the chemical operation of nitration is done with very great care (Fig. 21).

Halogenation

Halogenation, that is the combination of a substance with fluorine, chlorine, bromine or iodine (the group of elements which are called "halogens"), is often a useful intermediate step in chemical synthesis. The metal halides are such chemical salts as sodium chloride or potassium bromide. Halogenation is most commonly employed in chemical manufacture in

transforming organic compounds of carbon. Chloroform is a
well-known organic halide which is of value for its own sake,
but a halogen atom is frequently attached to a large organic
molecule at a particular point in its structure where it is desired
later to build in some further part of a still more complex
molecular structure.

Sulphonation

Another unit process is called sulphonation. This process is
less fundamental than oxidation or reduction, but it is important

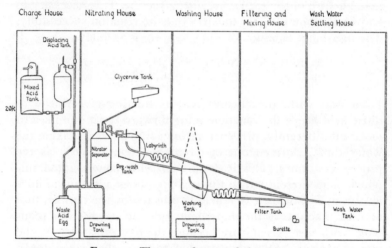

FIG. 21.   The manufacture of nitro-glycerine

because it happens to be useful. As it happens, the complexities
of molecular physics allow the group of atoms H_2SO_3, to exist
either as $HO\cdot SO\cdot OH$. (sulphur*ous* acid) or as $H\cdot SO_2\cdot OH$
(sulphon*ic* acid). Now although sulphon*ic* acid, H_2SO_4, ($HO\cdot$
$SO_2\cdot OH$) reacts with alkalis by exchanging its two hydrogen
atoms to form sulphates it can instead exchange -OH and
react with organic carbon structures such as benzene or naphthalene or aniline to produce what are called "aromatic"
sulphonic acids. We might think that all this is much too
complicated and detailed for a book of this kind, were it not
for the fact that benzene-sulphonic acid can be used as the first

stage of a chain of compounds leading to picric acid, used at one time as a military explosive. It can also be made to produce phenol (that is, carbolic acid) which is an important ingredient in making modern plastics. Benzene-disulphonic acid (that is, with two —SO$_3$H sulphonic acid groups) is an intermediate compound for the ultimate synthesis of a number of dyes. Fourthly and (for the moment) lastly, the sulphonic acid of aniline is sulphanilic acid which is the basis of sulphonamide and all the family of the potent "sulpha" drugs.

Diazotisation

Another unit process in chemistry, as it is used today, is diazotisation. This is worth mentioning for a number of reasons. To start with, it was discovered by a chemist called Griess who did a great deal of work on it while employed by Allsopps' brewery at Burton-on-Trent in the 1860s. Diazotisation has absolutely nothing to do with brewing, so that is indeed fortunate for chemical science that Messrs Allsopp did not bother too much what their chemist did in his spare time. The "diazo" reaction is important from two points of view. Firstly, it threw a good deal of light on the theoretical factors which control the structure of organic chemicals and led to a clearer understanding of how different substances can be built up from the same atoms—that is, how the atoms in organic molecules may under appropriate circumstances be twisted into different shapes. The second importance of the diazo reaction is that it produces substances that are of practical usefulness.

Just as more than one acid is built round sulphur, as we have seen, sulphuric acid giving sulph*ates* and sulphurous acid producing sulph*ites*, so also can more than one acid be constructed round nitrogen. Nitric acid, HNO$_3$, gives nitr*ates*, for example potassium nitrate, KNO$_3$ (saltpetre). On the other hand, HNO$_2$, nitrous acid, yields salts called nitr*ites*. Potassium nitrite, KNO$_2$, was discovered by the German chemist, Scheele, in 1774. Diazo compounds contain two joined nitrogen atoms in their molecules. These nitrogen atoms are, as it were, twisted around their linking electron shells in such a way that they are fixed to each other at two points. The result of this somewhat strained arrangement is that the molecule is, as the chemist puts it, highly reactive. Indeed, many dry diazo compounds are explosive.

The process by which diazo compounds are formed—that is diazotisation—is to treat an "aromatic" compound already containing a $-NH_2$ grouping (technically called "a primary amine"), for example aniline, with nitrous acid in the presence of a mineral acid such as hydrochloric acid. Then, where the $-NH_2$ group was before—visualised as $-N\big\langle^H_H$—a diazo group is produced instead, like this: $-N{=}N-$. As it was with sulphonation, so it is also with diazotisation. The technical chemist looking after the process must, as they say in patents, be well acquainted with "the art." That is, he must know what he is doing or he will not achieve his result and may even blow himself up. The usefulness of the operation is three-fold. Diazo-compounds are commercially valuable in making dyes and they are valuable as explosives. Beyond this, because the strained arrangement of doubly linked nitrogen atoms is highly reactive, diazotisation is a convenient operation midway through a complicated synthesis, when the chemist wants to attach a further block of atoms to a complicated structure. He uses the reactive diazo nitrogen as a convenient point of attachment for whatever molecular group he wants to introduce.

I could go on listing a whole series of further useful "unit processes" in chemistry. For example, *hydrolysis* in which a molecule of water, H-OH, takes part in a reaction; or *condensation* when molecules are caused to aggregate together; and many more. It is, however, perhaps sufficient to say that behind all the complexities of the infinite number of possible chemical reactions—and the mammoth publication known to chemists as "Beilstein" comprising a massive row of closely printed books about three times as extensive as the *Encyclopaedia Britannica* contains a list of only the *organic* compounds: the inorganic ones are left out—behind all these, there lies a group of chemical "laws." These say: (1) that the chemical elements combine in certain recognisable ways; (2) that the elements possess distinctive weights and that, when vapourised, unit volumes of their gases contain the same number of molecules; and, most important of all, (3) that the physical structure of the chemical atoms is made up of negatively charged electrons circulating in orbits around a positively charged nucleus.

In 1800 the Italian scientist Volta showed that certain kinds of chemical reactions could be arranged to release electrical energy. This is the so-called electric battery. A great discovery that still remains to be made is how to achieve the conversion of potential chemical energy directly into electrical energy on a large scale!

But even though this theoretically possible application of chemical theory has not yet been worked out, chemical laws and principles as they are understood today are, as everybody can see, used for a wide variety of practical purposes. In the next few chapters of this book I shall try to describe a few of these applications and their relation to the underlying scientific principles upon which they are based.

4

Chemistry and Metals

We have already referred to the fact that things that are wound up tend to run down. In chemistry this implies that reactions that can give off energy tend in the end to do so. And when energy is once lost the substance that has lost it remains dormant and stable unless some outside agency does something about it. Coal, for example, burns to ashes (plus gaseous carbon dioxide) and the cold ashes remain stable—for ever. Living creatures, ourselves like the rest of creation, can only maintain our energy by getting energy from food. As Lavoisier showed one hundred and fifty years ago, life is a chemical function and the energy we get is derived from oxidising the carbon and hydrogen in food, with the consequent production of "ashes," namely H_2O or water (plus, once again, carbon dioxide). The source of this energy that keeps us, and our earth, going is the light of the sun (developed from atomic, not chemical, power) that works the process of photosynthesis in green leaves. This photosynthesis is basically the chemical "reduction" of carbon dioxide—that is oxidised carbon—back to carbon, or to hydrogenated carbon, namely the carbohydrate sugar.

I have already said, the controlled oxidation of fuel in living animals is, in its final net result, the same as the more abrupt oxidation of burning, or the even slower oxidation of rusting iron. And since "reduced" substances give up energy when they become oxidised, Newton's law as well as our common knowledge that wound up systems tend to unwind, tells us that we are likely to find oxidised materials lying about on the surface of this oxygen-clad world.

In fact this is so. Iron, for example, is widely distributed in nature. But it does not occur as the metallic iron we need for our industrial uses. Instead it is found principally in the form of ferrous oxide (FeO) (Fe is the chemical symbol for iron), or as the black magnetic oxide (Fe_3O_4), or as ferric oxide (Fe_2O_3). Hence when we want to get back the reduced iron from these oxides we need to restore the energy the iron has lost. Should we, I wonder, find it remarkable or not that in looking for a source of energy to feed back into the oxidised iron we go to the identical source from which we ourselves obtain energy, that is, the reduced carbon from the sun's photosynthesis? The Great Weald of England was denuded of its dense forests to provide charcoal to smelt iron.

Although combustion with oxygen, that is the chemical process of oxidation, is the basic process by which chemical energy is released in this world and the substance oxidised brought to a more extreme state of inertia, there are other possibilities as well. Thus, while there are few metals that exist in the free state in nature—gold is one; it can sometimes be found as nuggets, or as veins running through quartz rocks— there are some "ores" that contain other forms of metal than the common oxide. The most common metal compound is one with sulphur. This is not surprising when it is remembered that sulphur is the next member, in atomic structure, of the same group as oxygen. Other combinations are with arsenic or silicon.

When ores containing metals, say iron or copper, are first discovered, the layers nearest the surface are usually simple oxides or a not widely different oxidised form of carbonate. Carbonates are combinations with the radical -CO_3 which, as is the nature of radicals, behaves as if it were a simple element. As the ore—particularly copper—is pursued to greater depth its character usually changes and the carbonates and oxides are replaced by sulphide, which presents a more troublesome chemical problem in recovering the metal.

Copper

The separation of sulphur combined with metal in ore, although troublesome, is not a particularly complicated chemical manoeuvre. For example, in the Rio Tinto copper mines in Spain, where immense quantities of copper are recovered, the ore is crushed and allowed to lie in the sun exposed to air and water for a period of months. In this leisurely process, the oxygen of the air combines with the sulphur. The chemical change is, in its essential features, from the *sulphide*, Cu_2S, to the *sulphate*, $2CuSO_4$. (In actual fact, as nature always tends to be more complicated than theory, copper often occurs mixed with other metals. Even when it is found as copper—in Sweden, in the Ural mountains and near Lake Superior in America—it is contaminated with small amounts of silver, bismuth and lead. The commonest compounds with sulphur are the elegantly named *chalcopyrite* or copper pyrites, $CuFeS_2$, and the still more romantic *erubescite*, Cu_3FeS_3, which is, as can be seen, a mixture of the sulphides of copper and iron.)

In principle, the recovery of metallic copper from its ore is, like the baking of scones, a simple chemical operation. But in practice both operations require a good deal of skill. To deal with an oxide, say the mineral cuprite, Cu_2O, one needs merely to roast the ore with carbon. The carbon then becomes *oxidised*, CO_2 is formed, the oxygen being picked up from the cuprite. Or, to express the same thing in converse terms, the copper is *reduced*.

To deal with the sulphur-containing pyrites, the chemist must first arrange for conditions to produce *oxidation* and then, at a later stage, *reduction*. As can well be imagined, this requires a considerable degree of technical adroitness. The principle, however, is simple. First, one needs to know, as a piece of interesting information, that sulphur sticks to copper more tightly than to iron. To start with, therefore, the ore is heated up well exposed to air. The iron in the pyrites releases itself from the sulphur to become oxidised and to turn itself into iron oxide, FeO. The copper clings on to the sulphur, as the people operating the process, possessing as they do the piece of information mentioned above, knew it would. To get rid of the iron, the operator now adds silica and goes on heating. Iron silicate, $FeSiO_3$, forms a slag that floats on the red-hot mixture and can be skimmed off. To convert the remaining copper sulphide, Cu_2S, to copper, the man in charge merely roasts it some more in the presence of air. The tendency of things to oxidise, given the opportunity, is such that the heat causes the sulphur to become sulphur dioxide, SO_2. Put the other way round, one can say that the sulphur reduces the copper to its metallic state.

For people who find it easier to follow this process from the shorthand of common chemical notation, the equations for the metallurgy of copper are as follows:

1. Pyrites roasted on the flat hearth of the furnace (iron oxidised).

$$2CuFeS_2 + 4O_2 \longrightarrow Cu_2S + 2FeO + 3SO_2$$

Copper   Oxygen   Copper   Iron   Sulphur dioxide
pyrites   from air   sulphide   oxide   gas

2. Roasted ore heated in "reverberatory" furnace with added silica.

$$FeO + SiO_2 \longrightarrow FeSiO_3$$

Iron oxide   Silica   Iron silicate (slag, run off as a top layer)

3. Residual copper "matte" ("coarse metal") reheated.

(a) $$2Cu_2S + 3O_2 \longrightarrow 2Cu_2O + 2SO_2$$

Copper   Oxygen   Copper   Sulphur
sulphide   from air   oxide   dioxide

(b) $$Cu_2S + 2Cu_2O \longrightarrow 6Cu + SO_2$$

Copper   Copper   Sulphur
oxide   dioxide

When you make a sponge cake in the kitchen, you first beat up the butter and sugar as vigorously as possible in order to mix as much air as you can with the batter. Next, when the egg is added, the cook takes pains to "fold" it in quietly *without* adding air. If she does not, the cake is a failure. In smelting copper, rather the same principles apply. The ore, sinking through the furnace, comes to the section where it meets the air blast. This is where reaction 3 (a) occurs (oxidation). When it falls past this point into the bottom part of the furnace, it passes the air blast and reaction 3 (b) then comes about (reduction).

The neat chemical reactions shown in the equations given above are, of course, just a little too good to be true. In actual fact the copper produced by equation 3 (b) is usually full of bubbles and, besides this, may contain about two per cent. of impurities. It is, consequently, subjected to various purification processes. If it is simply melted on a furnace hearth, oxygen from the air dissolves in it and forms slag with impurities such as iron, which can then be skimmed off combined with silicate. The small amount of copper oxide produced at the same time is got rid of in a manner that is of some general chemical interest.

The basis of biological chemistry is, as I have pointed out before, the use of reduced carbon—in the form of sugar or starch or other nutrients—which becomes oxidised by the air we breathe giving up energy with the resultant production of CO_2 and H_2O as well. In exactly the same way, the oxidised copper is "pushed back," as it were, into the reduced state by the use of a vegetable "foodstuff," also made up of carbon and hydrogen. The process is called "poling." It consists of pushing poles of green wood into the molten metal. Torrents of reducing gas containing methane, CH_4, are produced by the great heat and, bubbling up through the liquid copper, reduce any traces of copper oxide, Cu_2O, to copper with the formation of CO_2 and H_2O.

Oxidation and reduction are processes that are fundamental to the science of chemistry. A great deal of modern study has been devoted to the phenomenon and *oxidation-reduction potentials*—that is the measure of the tendency of different chemical systems to move either towards the oxidised or the reduced state—have been worked out in mathematical detail. This modern understanding of chemical principle is important for the future progress of chemistry, yet it must be admitted that the practice of smelting and refining copper (like the practice of making good sponge cake) has been known since ancient times, for example, since the civilisation of Babylon in about 4000 B.C.

In order to obtain copper of the highest degree of purity, for use for example as power cables for carrying electric current, the process of *electrolysis* is used. This takes advantage of the properties of ions that we discussed in the last chapter. Ordinary un-ionised copper is the shining auburn metal we know. When it is dissolved in sulphuric acid it becomes *ionised* and in the liquid—now bright blue—we have copper ions, Cu^{++}, and sulphate ions $SO_4^{=}$. A solution of copper sulphate is electrically neutral because the copper ions, doubly charged positively, are counter-balanced by an equal number of sulphate ions, doubly charged negatively. If, however, two electrodes are dipped into the solution and an electrical potential applied across them from an outside source of power, the positively charged copper ions are drawn to the negative electrode, the so-called *cathode*, where they lose their electric charge, cease in consequence to be ions and find themselves instead turned back into copper.

The operation of purifying copper by electrolysis is done like this: the blocks of impure copper are hung in an acid bath and are used as the positive *anode* from which the injected current

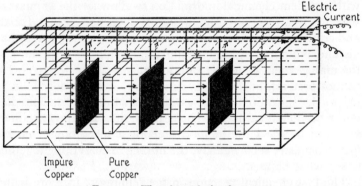

FIG. 22.   The electrolysis of copper

flows. The copper dissolves in the acid and the copper ions are carried through the liquid to a series of thin sheets of pure copper which are made the *cathode*. Consequently as the crude copper blocks dwindle away the thin copper sheets become bigger. Impurities such as iron, nickel, cobalt, arsenic and zinc dissolve in the acid but fail to keep up with copper ions in the race to get themselves deposited on the cathode and fall to the bottom of the bath as *anode slime*. Electrolytic copper, as it is called, is anything up to 99·99 per cent. pure. The arrangement of the apparatus is shown in Fig. 22.

Iron and Steel

We are all fully aware today that the status of any nation in the modern world depends on the amount of metal of one sort

or another that it produces. A hill of copper can put Chuqui-
camata, Chile, on the map; the gold mines of South Africa
contribute to that nation's economic strength; the nickel
deposits of Sudbury, Ontario, make Canada the envy of her
neighbours; but the metal above all others upon which our
modern technological civilisation rests is iron. And while the
techniques of iron refining and its conversion into different
types of useable metal are complicated and difficult, the
chemistry involved is basically simple. Once again just as we
have seen for copper, it involves a judicious manipulation of the
two chemical processes of oxidation and of reduction, together
with sufficient chemical information to allow for the admixture
with the iron of appropriate amounts of carbon, nickel, cobalt
and certain other substances. The scientist can justly claim that
his understanding of basic chemical principles is important to
the management of modern blast furnaces and converters. He
cannot pretend, however, that conscious scientific forethought
led to the invention of, for example, stainless steel. This has
never been claimed to have been more than a happy accident
achieved by the same method used by a schoolboy given his
first "chemistry set," namely, the mixing of everything together
to see what happens.

The first chemical reaction in the refining of iron ore is the
reduction of the iron by carbon monoxide, CO, produced from
coke by the heat of the blast furnace. A related chemical change
is the combination of a proportion of the hot carbon with the
iron to produce a carbon-iron compound melting at a lower
and more convenient temperature than that at which pure iron
melts. These reactions can be written as follows:

1. Coke burning at very high temperature in the air blast of the fur-
   nace $2C + O_2 \longrightarrow 2CO$
2. Reduction of haematite ore (Fe_2O_3) $Fe_2O_3 + 3CO \longrightarrow 2Fe + 3CO_2$
3. Conversion of reduced iron to pig
   iron $3Fe + 2CO \longrightarrow Fe_3C + CO_2$

We have already commented upon the fact that in real life
chemistry is seldom as simple as it appears to be in textbooks.
Potatoes, we are told, are starchy food. Quite true, so they are.

But they also contain protein and vitamins, mineral salts and water. Iron ore, too, contains something more than Fe_2O_3. An average ore may contain from 25 to 33 per cent. of oxidised iron but there may be present as well 12 per cent. of silica, 10 per cent. of alumina, 5 per cent. of lime, and smaller amounts of sulphur and phosphorus. And if you are making piano wire (or wrought iron) with a purity of 99·8 to 99·9 per cent. you need to get rid of these extraneous materials.

For many years, limestone has been added to the charge of iron ore and coke put into the blast furnace. The chemical reason for adding it is that it combines with the silica in the ore to form a glass-like material that floats on the molten iron and can consequently be drawn off separately as slag. This is a back-to-front application of the same idea by which iron is separated from copper in copper refining. The chemistry of the process is shown in the equation below as a fourth reaction taking place in the blast furnace:

4. Formation of lava-like slag.

$$CaCO_3 \longrightarrow CaO + CO_2$$
Limestone   Lime

$$CaO + SiO_2 \longrightarrow CaSiO_3$$
Lime   Silica   Slag
(in ore)

The management of the "flux," that is the added limestone, and the balancing of conditions of temperature and air in the blast furnace to suit the particular kind of ore being treated are matters of great skill. Indeed, the process might almost be viewed as an art rather than a science. The proportion of impurities remaining in the pig iron has an important effect on the physical properties of the iron produced. Traces of residual sulphur (which should be driven off as SO_2 gas) tend to cause cast iron to crack. Silicon, too, causes the carbon in the iron to crystallise as graphite (this is the "lead" in pencils) which is responsible for the grey fractures which sometimes occur in castings. The proportion of carbon also has a very significant effect on the hardness of the iron. The problem of carbon is quite complicated because not only is the amount present in the iron important, but there is also a difference depending on whether it is chemically combined as Fe$_3$C to give "white iron" or simply mixed in as graphite to produce "grey iron" (Fig. 23).

The extraordinary simplicity of many of the economically

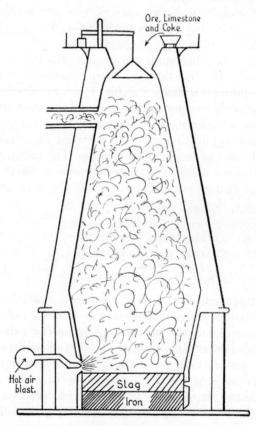

Ore, Limestone and Coke.

Hot air blast.

Slag

Iron

FIG. 23.   A blast furnace

important scientific discoveries is a constant surprise—at least to people who live a generation or so after each discovery has been made. On the face of it, there does not seem to be very much chemistry in the separation of impurities from iron ore as slag. And yet, up to the year 1876 the traditional operation of adding limestone to combine as a molten-glass-like silicon compound possessed one fundamental weakness; it failed to deal with the impurity, phosphorus.

Right up until the beginning of the present century the great deposits of iron ore in Lorraine, upon which Europe principally depends for iron and steel today, could not be used and were, in consequence, quite valueless—all because no way was known of getting rid of the comparatively large amount of phosphorus mixed with the iron. Now, in a single year, up to forty million tons of iron have been extracted, and smelted with coke produced in the Ruhr.

Pig iron from a blast furnace, although reduced and freed from much of the impurities of the original ore, is nevertheless still far from pure iron. It contains, for example, quite a substantial amount of carbon. The traditional process for purifying it further and obtaining the strong and useful material for engineering construction known as wrought iron was to get as much slag as possible out of it by heating it in a small reverberatory furnace and then to "puddle" it by stirring the molten mass about. Chemically, this was one more example of *reduction* of iron and *oxidation* of excess carbon, thus:

$$Fe_3C + FeO \longrightarrow 4Fe + CO \text{ (carbon monoxide gas)}$$

Later, this process, comparatively simple as it would seem in chemical terms but complicated and difficult and skilled in technical execution, was displaced by mechanisation in the Bessemer converter, invented in 1856. The essential feature of the Bessemer process was to blow air through the molten pig iron contained in a steel pot lined with fire-brick. This caused the silicon and manganese impurities to "burn" up into slag. Chemically this is merely oxidation to SiO_2 and MnO. Part of the iron is oxidised and so finally is the carbon. Like more familiar kinds of "burning," the reaction produces heat. When it is finished and the flames coming from the pot die down, there comes the principal novelty of the process. The pot is set up on a spindle and is at this stage tipped over on to its side. Appropriate amounts of manganese, silicon and carbon are added, in the form of ferromanganese, ferrosilicon and anthracite, to mop up the excess of oxygen left in the molten mass as bubbles from the blast, and to give the appropriate composition to the steel it is designed finally to produce (Fig. 24).

There is nothing particularly strange to us today in the idea of a needle with its eye at the point end. Yet the notion of putting it there—without which the sewing machine is impossible—was a revolutionary intellectual conception. Similarly, Bessemer's idea of a pocket blast furnace capable of being tipped about like a butter churn seemed ridiculous to the conservative steel man of his day and years of experimentation were needed before his process became a commercial success.

But the Bessemer process as it first came into use could not deal with phosphorus; low-phosphorus ores are rare and costly (at least in Europe), and there lay the tantalising and unuseable riches of the Lorraine ore beds. Attempts were first made to force the chemical process by which the manganese, the silicon and the carbon were each oxidised by the air blast to slag (SiO_2, MnO) plus carbon monoxide gas, to go on and oxidise the phosphorus as well. But when, in an attempt to do this, the blast was continued after the flames of burning carbon monoxide had died down, as fast as the phosphorus was oxidised, it oxidised the iron and became itself reduced again. The result was that the iron, which it was the whole purpose of the process to produce, "wasted away" and, besides, ate into the sand and clay lining of the Bessemer pot and ruined it.

The piece of chemistry discovered in 1876 by Sidney Thomas and Percy Gilchrist seems ridiculously simple now that we know it. But it was of immense economic importance at the time it was made. Sand is an oxidation product of the element silicon. Its composition is SiO_2. When SiO_2 is fused with, say, sodium carbonate under appropriate conditions, it is converted to sodium silicate, Na_2SiO_3. This is a salt of silicic acid. It is fairly obvious, therefore, that the final residue formed when pig iron is treated in a converter lined with sand will be an *acid* slag. Thomas and Gilchrist tried the effect of lining the pot of the converter with *basic* (that is alkaline) substances such as burned limestone or dolomite (mixed carbonates of magnesium and calcium). At the same time they added some burned lime to the charge of pig iron. Lo and behold, when the conditions were thus rendered basic instead of acid, oxides of phosphorus produced during the "blow" were retained in the slag with the other impurities and, besides, the converter lining was not damaged. As one more additional reward for this simple, clearcut, chemical invention, the basic slag which results during the manufacture of this "Thomas steel," containing as it does substantial amounts of phosphorus, is a valuable fertiliser.

Although much of metal chemistry in general and the chemistry of iron in particular is in principle the *reduction* of

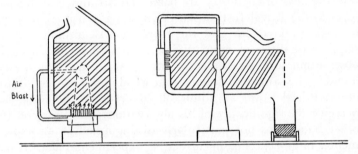

FIG. 24. A Bessemer converter

oxidised metal from its ores and the parallel *oxidation* of the contaminating materials eventually removed as slag, the metallurgical art, if it may be so called, also involves the mixing of appropriate amounts of supplementary ingredients. Pig iron is comparatively impure. It contains 3–4 per cent. of carbon, nearly as much silicon, and varying amounts of manganese, phosphorus and sulphur. Wrought iron after having been "puddled" only contains 0·1–0·2 per cent. of carbon. Steel is an iron mixture almost free from phosphorus, sulphur and silicon but containing more carbon than wrought iron. Tool steel, for example, contains between 0·9 and 1·5 per cent. of carbon, structural steel 0·2–0·6 per cent., and mild steel about 0·2 per cent.

Among more modern iron mixtures is manganese steel, containing 7–20 per cent. of manganese. This is very hard and is used, for example, for making burglar-proof safes. Chromium-vanadium steels have about 1 per cent. of chromium and 0·1 per cent. of vanadium added to them; they have greater tensile strength. Tungsten steel contains 8–20 per cent. of tungsten plus 3–5 per cent. of chromium, and is suitable for making high-speed tools. Nickel steel contains 2·4 per cent. of nickel and is used for armour plate. And so on.

The science of chemistry is the collection of information from nature and from experiment about the composition of matter. The mass of facts thus collected must then be correlated into some sort of system, for it is upon such systematic correlation that the laws of chemistry are based. Dr Strathdee, in his lectures to the Royal Institute of Chemistry given in Edinburgh in 1954, pointed out that the correlation of assembled data requires qualities of mind different from those employed in observation and experiment. Both qualities are not always found in the same individual. Some excel in the one, not in the other. Priestley was an admirable observer but he could not perceive the significance of his observations; Lavoisier, on the other hand, was not particularly distinguished as an experimenter but he excelled in correlating experimental facts. It was he who appreciated the significance of Priestley's discovery of oxygen and gave, in 1778, the true interpretation of the process of combustion.

Today an enormous amount of systematic, planned research is carried out. But sometimes an advance is achieved through accident because an investigator is sufficiently alert and well trained to appreciate that something unusual has occurred. "Chance," Pasteur once said, "only visits the prepared mind."

Just before the 1914–1918 war a metallurgist, Mr Harry Brearley, was studying the wear of rifle barrels. Among other experimental alloys, he prepared one of steel containing a higher proportion of chromium than had been used before. Like many others of his sample steels, it was put through a routine series of mechanical tests and found to be unsatisfactory. Along with other pieces of metal, it was subsequently discarded and thrown on the scrap heap. A fortnight later, one of Mr Brearley's assistants happened to observe that while rust had attacked the majority of the steel specimens in the dump, the alloy containing the higher chromium content had remained bright. Immediately a knife was forged and tested by being left in Mr Brearley's garden for a fortnight. No rusting took place. Stainless steel had been discovered.

Aluminium

Like most other metals, aluminium occurs in nature in an oxidised form. The most familiar ore is bauxite, which is found in British Guiana and Ghana, as $Al_2O_3 \cdot 2H_2O$, is comparatively free from diluents such as silica. We modern people find aluminium an extremely useful metal—for making aircraft (it is only one-third the weight of iron), for making cooking pots, "silver" paper, toothpaste tubes, aluminium paint, prefabricated houses and all sorts of other things. The use of aluminium is, however, very recent. It was, in fact, introduced to the public only in 1855 at the Paris Exposition. The reason why it was not exploited as a metal before is that it is impossible to smelt its ores. And the reason why it cannot be smelted is that its affinity for oxygen—that is, its tendency to become oxidised —is so great that there is no convenient substance available to reduce it. In particular, reduced carbon which, in the form of charcoal or of coke, is used to smelt the commoner and historically available metals like iron or copper, has less attraction for oxygen than has the aluminium itself.

The striking affinity of aluminium for oxygen is seen when aluminium powder is strongly heated. It then burns with a brilliant light in the same way as does the magnesium powder once used in flashlight photography. Thermite incendiary bombs are made of aluminium. By a most happy circumstance, however, under normal conditions of moderate temperature only the surface film of a piece of metallic aluminium eagerly and instantly combines with oxygen as would be expected, and this first layer forms a close-fitting, continuous and impervious skin of aluminium oxide that protects the substance of, let us say, an aluminium teapot from spontaneous combustion!

A great deal of troublesome chemistry had to be done before a practical method of preparing aluminium metal in bulk was discovered. The first laboratory process was devised in 1825, but it involved the reaction between aluminium chloride and an "amalgam," or blend, of metallic potassium and mercury. The metallic potassium used was itself produced with some difficulty by the electrolysis of fused caustic potash. When the mercury was distilled away, a residue of somewhat impure aluminium remained. The process was slightly improved in 1827 by the German chemist Wöhler, who managed to obtain little pieces of aluminium metal about as big as pinheads by the direct reaction of metallic potassium on aluminium chloride. About twenty-five years after this another improvement involving the use of sodium instead of potassium was introduced in France.

The modern method of obtaining aluminium from the aluminium salts in which it occurs in nature depends on the process of electrolysis which we have already described as being used in the purification of copper. But even this application of what one might conceive to be a straightforward chemical principle is in practice complicated with so reactive a metal as aluminium. If one goes at it like a bull at a gate—as with copper for example—instead of being able to dissolve the aluminium salt in an acid solution in water, to pass a current through it and to recover the metal ion at the cathode, the aluminium carried by the current to the cathode breaks down water (H^+OH^-, or H_2O) when it gets there and, instead of metal, one obtains aluminium hydroxide, $Al(OH)_3$, and hydrogen gas.

In science, as in so many other human activities, hindsight is much easier than foresight. The systematic collection of facts does indeed enable the scientist to work out the "laws" of chemistry. And these "laws" undoubtedly enable the chemist to foresee in a logical way how to do new chemical things. Nevertheless a little intuition and perhaps some luck as well are useful ingredients for discovery.

The modern electrolytic method of producing aluminium was discovered almost simultaneously in the United States by Charles Martin Hall, and in France by Paul Héroult—both in 1886. The essence of the process that is used to this day is as follows. Purified alumina, Al_2O_3, is dissolved in molten cryolite. Cryolite is an aluminium ore found only in Greenland and is a double compound of sodium fluoride and aluminium fluoride. Cryolite is odd stuff. It occurs in colourless or snow-white masses. Occasionally, if there is a trace of iron oxide in it, it is brown or red or even black. It is usually translucent. One of its most peculiar properties is that it melts readily, even in the flame of a candle. The Eskimos can therefore be forgiven for taking it to be a peculiar kind of ice.

The alumina and molten cryolite are melted together in a steel box lined with carbon. Carbon rods or blocks are dipped into the molten mass and used as the anode from which electric current flows through to the bottom of the box which is arranged as the cathode. The aluminium cations, Al^{+++}, are carried by the current and deposited as metallic aluminium at the cathode. At the temperature of 950° C. at which the process is operated, liquid metallic aluminium is heavier than liquid cryolite and so it stays at the bottom as a layer of metal. The oxide anions, $O^=$, are brought to the anode and appear as oxygen. At the high temperature, however, this oxygen burns up the carbon rods of which the anode is composed and is consequently dissipated as carbon dioxide. Thus the process, though dependent on the energy of large electric currents, is to some extent a kind of smelting after all.

The steel boxes used are often 20 ft. long, 6 ft. wide and about 3 ft. deep. They are commonly arranged in lines. Each box may use 20,000 to 50,000 amperes of electricity. Additional alumina can be added while the process is going on and molten aluminium is drawn off periodically (Fig. 25).

The production of metallic aluminium, while presenting special difficulties due to its strong affinity for oxygen, is thus, like the winning of most metals—except the few inert "noble" metals like gold that can exist in the native state—a chemical exercise in reduction. Much of the remainder of the metallurgical processes to which it is subjected are, as with iron and copper, merely skilled technology involving, like cake-making, the discovery of what mixtures give the desired result for the purpose in view. A proportion of silicon amounting to 5–20 per cent. is added to aluminium to assist the process of casting. Aluminium-zinc and aluminium-copper mixtures are also used for various purposes, the latter in making motor-car pistons. Aluminium-magnesium alloys possess increased strength and ductility, and a mixture of aluminium containing 1·25 per cent. of manganese is used for making saucepans. The structural supports of aeroplanes are commonly composed of "duralumin,"

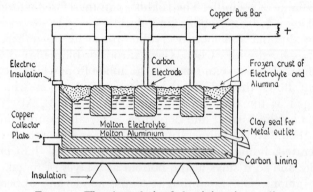

FIG. 25.   The electrolysis of aluminium in cryolite
By permission from *The Chemical Process Industries*, 2nd ed., by R. W. Shreve.
Copyright 1956.   McGraw-Hill Book Co.

which contains 4–5 per cent. of copper, 0·6–1·2 per cent. of magnesium and 0·6–1·2 per cent. of manganese. And there are many other aluminium alloys.

Magnesium

Aluminium, although by far the most important metal whose oxide cannot be reduced by the ordinary methods of smelting with carbon, is not alone in this characteristic. There is, indeed, a group of metals presenting the same practical difficulty. Magnesium, which is even lighter than aluminium, is obtained like aluminium by electrolysis, in this case, however, of a bath of molten magnesium chloride. Like aluminium, magnesium powder or ribbon combines avidly with oxygen and burns with a bright light. Nowadays, however, it is of importance not so much for fireworks or flash powder as in aircraft manufacture. Not only is it used for making landing wheels, engine crank-cases, propeller blades and suchlike, but magnesium sheet is also employed for the stressed-skin type of wing construction (Fig. 26). Much of the magnesium produced, particularly in the United States, is derived from sea water. By treating sea water (containing about 0·13 per cent. of Mg.) with slaked lime $(Ca(OH)_2)$, magnesium hydroxide $Mg (OH)_2$ is formed. This is insoluble and sinks to the bottom. When it has been recovered it is treated with hydrochloric acid to convert it to the magnesium chloride from which the metal is derived.

Calcium, sodium, potassium and beryllium are other metals which are recovered by this same process of electrolysis from a

FIG. 26.   Aircraft with stressed magnesium skin

bath of molten salts. It is not necessary to specify the details of the process used for each. In all of them the underlying chemical process is designed to achieve reduction without using burning carbon in one form or another. A further complication is the need to avoid the presence of water while applying electrolysis as the method for forcing the metal cations away from the anion radicals with which they are combined.

Chromium

But there are still other useful metals whose chemistry is even more inconvenient than that of the group comprising aluminium, magnesium and these others. Chromium, for example, is difficult to reduce, and moreover possesses a strong tendency to combine with carbon to form chromium carbide. Yet it is nowadays an important metal, for chromium plating, for making resistance wires for such products as electric fires, for making stainless steel and other alloys. Chromite ores, usually made up of the oxide, Cr_2O_3, are found in Cuba, Russia, Rhodesia and Turkey—to name the biggest producing areas. To reduce them while at the same time avoiding the use of carbon, chemists have hit on the logical method of using metallic aluminium as the reducing agent. And so we have the process called "aluminothermic reduction." This consists of mixing the chromic oxide with finely divided aluminium and heating it until the mixture ignites. The burning aluminium picks up the oxygen from the chromic oxide, while at the same time the heat generated is sufficient to melt the metal produced so that it can be poured out directly into moulds.

Today we are all acutely aware that modern civilisation depends on metals. A nation's place in the world, whether it is powerful and respected or weak and insignificant, depends to a large measure on the magnitude of its steel production. But failing steel, a mountain of copper or a supply of aluminium or chromium or—for a rather different reason—gold, are valuable contributions to national wealth. Recently the possession of workable amounts of uranium has also become an important economic asset. In passing, it should perhaps be mentioned that uranium is much commoner than is usually imagined and is actually more plentiful than silver, mercury or iodine. But although it is found in various types of rocks and in sea water, the sources from which it is most readily recovered are the pitchblende deposits of the Belgian Congo and the Great Bear Lake in Canada. Uranium metal looks like steel but combines with oxygen even more avidly than either aluminium or magnesium; indeed in the form of metallic powder it may spontaneously burst into flames. Fortunately, perhaps, it is not used as metal so that there is little need for chemists to work out a method for smelting it. Its extraction even as uranium oxide is, however, rather complicated because it is usually mixed with a number of other substances. The extraction process is based on leaching with acid followed by precipitation of uranium salts from the acid solution.

There is no need to labour further the fact that modern

civilisation depends on metals. It is quite clear that the part of chemistry that deals with metals is of fundamental importance to our daily life. Metal chemistry has three basic divisions. Firstly, there is the knowledge of the *atomic structure* of each of the known metals, upon which their place in the periodic table of elements and their chemical behaviour depends. The second kind of chemistry upon which our command of metals is based is the process of *reduction* by which the metals are given back the energy they have lost in becoming oxidised—as does almost everything else in the world. This process of chemical reduction can be divided into two classes. In the first are those metals that can be smelted directly with charcoal or coke or some other form of carbon. For these metals, of which iron and copper are the most prominent, we use under the more drastic conditions of the blast furnace and the Bessemer converter the same basic chemistry that we and all living things (with some few exceptions such as sulphur bacteria) employ constantly to prevent ourselves from becoming oxidised and run down. It is true that we ourselves do not use elemental carbon or coke as food, but our sugars and starches and fats are reduced carbon, nevertheless, and are indeed the basis from which coke comes. The metals requiring the special chemical devices that we have just described are in a third class.

I hope that even in this simplified account enough has been said to show that although the principles of metal chemistry are simple, being basically those of *oxidiation* and *reduction* and mixing, the practice is often highly complex. And being complex and difficult, the practical processes of metallurgy are often empirical.

Having reached this point in our attempt to discuss what chemistry is about, it is appropriate to move on to another branch of applied chemistry which is also of enormous importance but which, we must admit with what diffidence we can command, is almost entirely rule-of-thumb. I refer to catalysis.

5

Catalysts and Chemistry

Boys and girls at school are taught the different kinds of chemical reactions that can take place when the different kinds of chemical substances, each with their different properties, interact with each other. All these have to be learned, just as the zoologist has to learn the characteristics that distinguish a stoat from a weasel or an entomologist has to know which particular mosquito carries malaria. This is only right and proper, since it is upon the varied reactions between the different substances that the broad generalisations—that is the "laws" of chemistry —are based. There are, however, many important and useful reactions that could in theory take place but don't. Or rather, they do not occur unless some agency is introduced to make them do so. Among these desirable reactions are such major operations as the production of petrol from coal, the manufacture of cooking fat from palm oil, and the manufacture of artificial fertiliser from air. Sulphuric acid, perhaps the most important of all heavy chemicals, is made by a chemical operation that does not, as it were, "go" by itself without special help. And one of the most important of our modern industries, the preparation of diverse organic chemicals from petroleum, requires the use of a "cat cracker." That is to say, like these other operations, it depends on a *catalyst.*

Catalysts are substances that bring about a reaction that might possibly happen without them, or might not. Or they make a very slow reaction take place quickly. For example, a man walking along the street might fall down. That is to say, the man, being in a vertical position, possesses enough potential energy to enable the reaction of falling down and hitting the pavement to take place. Under normal circumstances, however, it may never do so. But let a banana skin be introduced between the man and the pavement and it will act as a *catalyst*. When the man stands on it, the potential energy inherent in his vertical position is released, and down he goes. The banana skin itself is not much affected by the process and retains its power to release energy from a whole series of subsequent passers-by.

Catalysis and Sulphuric Acid

It always comes as a slight surprise to the layman to be told that sulphuric acid is a substance of importance to our modern industrial civilisation. Although no private citizen ever uses it and few people even know what it looks like unless they can remember seeing it when they were at school, it plays a part in the manufacture of practically every industrial product. For example, there are many drugs, dyes and explosives that need sulphuric acid for their manufacture. It is used in steel pickling (that is, the cleaning of steel preparatory to processing). The great rayon industry depends on a supply of sulphuric acid of high purity, and in agriculture the battle for food production to maintain an adequate level of nutrition for the ever-increasing population of the world would suffer a disastrous setback should there be a lack of sulphuric acid for the manufacture of superphosphate and other artificial fertilisers.

The compound H_2SO_4 is, of course, the sulphuric acid we have been talking about. It is so very useful as a chemical because it is the cheapest acid to produce. As an acid, it can be used to dissolve metals and other substances so that chemical reactions can be carried out upon them. It will react with basic substances to produce salts. It possesses the power of picking up water and can thus be employed as a dehydrating agent. And, furthermore, it can serve as an oxidising agent, giving up one of its oxygen atoms and itself becoming sulphurous acid, H_2SO_3.

And this fundamental chemical, supplies of which exert a crucial effect on the prices quoted on the commodity markets of the world, is produced in the present-day manner because vanadium in the form of vanadium pentoxide, V_2O_5, found in a peculiar geological formation near the insignificant village of Mottram in Cheshire and called mottramite (also occurring, it must be said, in other ores in Peru, Colorado, Rhodesia and one or two other places), possesses *catalytic* properties.

Sulphur can exist in several degrees of oxidation. The reduced form, that is elemental sulphur, is a comparatively stable yellow powder. Sulphur is the modern term for the brimstone of antiquity found bubbling and boiling in the nether regions of the pit. Or, to put it more prosaically, sulphur is often ejected from volcanoes. There are substantial deposits of sulphur in Spain, Italy, Chile, Japan and elsewhere. When sulphur is burned, it combines with atmospheric oxygen to form sulphur dioxide, SO_2. This is the familiar acrid gas that many of us remember as being produced in old-fashioned days when sulphur was burned in a saucer to fumigate a sickroom after a patient had finally been released from quarantine. When sulphur dioxide is dissolved in water it becomes sul-phur*ous* acid. The reaction is $SO_2 + H_2O \longrightarrow H_2SO_3$.

To produce sulphur*ic* acid, the SO_2 must be converted to SO_3 which, when it is combined with water, gives us what we want: H_2SO_4. Unfortunately, the easily produced gas SO_2 combines with oxygen at a rate so slow as to be almost imperceptible, although the reaction $2SO_2 + O_2 \longrightarrow 2SO_3$ when it does occur is accompanied by the release of a substantial amount of heat. The interesting point from the aspect of our present discussion is that when a *catalyst* is present, SO_2 combines with oxygen as briskly as you please. And just as a man can be caused to release kinetic energy by means of a banana skin or orange peel or, for that matter, a carelessly abandoned roller skate, so also can platinum powder, nickel or cobalt sulphates, or the oxides of tungsten, molybdenum, chromium or iron do the trick for sulphur dioxide. In actual practice, modern "contact process" sulphuric-acid plants use vanadium pentoxide, as I have said.

Sulphuric acid manufacturing plants are, in many ways, remarkably simple. Those that use sulphur carry out a process in which the sulphur is first melted and dried off. The molten sulphur is then pumped to a burner where it is combusted in a current of previously dried air. (As a matter of fact, the air is

usually dried by passing it through some of the sulphuric acid
that the factory makes: sulphuric acid, it will be remembered,
is a dehydrating agent.) The air is supplied to the burners by
blowers operating under a pressure of two or three pounds per
square inch greater than atmospheric pressure. This burning
process produces on a grand scale the SO_2 as used in fumigating.

The hot gases from the burners are a mixture of about 10 per
cent. of SO_2 with 90 per cent. of air. They are usually cooled to
about 400° C. from the temperature of 1200° C. or so at which
they leave the burners. The next part of the operation is to get
the chemical process $2SO_2 + O_2 \longrightarrow 2SO_3 +$ heat to take
place. Although, as I have said, this reaction hardly takes
place at all if the SO_2 and the oxygen are simply heated together, it can be made to occur quite rapidly by passing the
SO_2 and the oxygen at 400° C. through layers of vanadium
pentoxide spread out on shelves packed in vertical tubes. The
vanadium pentoxide takes no part in the chemical process. It is,
indeed, for this reason by definition a *catalyst*. It merely forms a
favourable environment, a sort of springboard, as it were, on
which the SO_2 and the oxygen get together. Since the combination of SO_2 and O_2 when it occurs is accompanied by heat, the
tubes containing the trays of vanadium pentoxide are all packed
into an insulated steel tank or tower called a converter. An
appropriate cooling system which keeps the reaction at its
optimum temperature of 400° C. draws off heat that can be
used to heat boilers to keep the plant going. And when one has
by this means got SO_3, all that needs to be done to turn it into
sulphuric acid is to allow it to absorb water (Fig. 27).

The whole process is, in principle, absurdly simple. Plants
capable of producing five or six hundred tons of sulphuric acid
a day can be run by one man. At the same time, considerably
more than a ton of high-pressure steam may be generated for
every ton of acid manufactured. No wonder that sulphuric acid
is cheap.

But—and this is the point of discussing the process in this
book—the entire performance, the chemical combination of S
with O_2, which could be expected from the atomic structure of
both oxygen and sulphur and their systematic positions in the

A.C.—7

periodic table of elements, the equally predictable combination
of SO_2 with oxygen to give SO_3, which does *not* happen, and the
economic and industrial importance of the sulphuric acid being
made—all these, or at least the possibility of converting the
key SO_2 into SO_3—depend on something which is up to now
outside the logic of chemical science. I refer to the necessity, for
no obviously explicable reason, of vanadium pentoxide.

The way catalysts work is not yet fully understood and for
this reason elementary chemical textbooks contain very little
reference to them. Nevertheless they are in practice of immense
importance. Chemists who actually perform these basic operations upon which whole industries depend—such as making

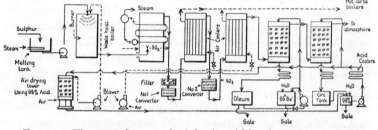

FIG. 27.   The manufacture of sulphuric acid by the contact process
By permission from *The Chemical Process Industries*, 2nd ed., by R. N. Shreve.
Copyright 1956.   The McGraw-Hill Book Co.

sulphuric acid, or petroleum chemicals, or fixing atmospheric
nitrogen to turn it into artificial fertiliser—must of course know
the principles of chemistry that the schoolboys learn. But if
SO_2 won't turn into SO_3 without the presence of vanadium
pentoxide derived from ore dug up near the village of Mottram
in Cheshire, then the practising industrial chemist will have to
make use of the V_2O_5 even if he does not understand exactly
how it does what it does.

Theories of Catalysis

As we shall need to consider in a later chapter, catalysis—
that is, how catalysts work—is of importance in other branches
of chemistry than sulphuric acid production or the manufacture of plastics. Indeed, in biochemistry, which comprises the

chemistry of living tissues, catalysis is of fundamental significance. Because of the importance of the subject, many first-class
scientists have tried, and with some success, to elucidate the
mode of operation by which catalysts achieve the results they
do.

Twenty-five years ago, say in the 1930s, the industrial
approach to this extremely important subject was still the *ad
hoc* method of trying every conceivable combination of metal
or oxide or sulphide to see whether it would work as a catalyst.
During the 1930s, however, there was a great deal of study of
the mechanics of what was called "the solid state" and some
knowledge was obtained of the atomic configuration of different
types of metals and what makes some substances good conductors of electricity and some poor conductors and what causes
some, called semi-conductors, to conduct currents better in one
direction than in the other. In the 1940s these ideas were
extended to some of the puzzles of catalysis and it was postulated, notably at a meeting of the Chemical Society in London
in 1949, that the behaviour of a substance as a catalyst depended
on the electronic configurations of its solid state. For example,
solids that catalyse oxidations and reductions are mostly electronic conductors, while catalysts for acid-alkali reactions are
non-conductors (in fact insulators).

Although the beginnings of a theory of how some catalysts
work is all to the good, there is much complex work and thinking still to be done before the laws of catalysis are all worked
out. In some instances, the action of catalysts is based on
"chemisorption." That is to say, the reacting substances appear
to be adsorbed on to the surface of the catalyst and their
valency bonds spread out, as it were, to enable them to react
with each other. The mathematics and physics of this theory,
although as yet incomplete, are becoming at least partly understood. But they apply only to solid catalysts acting on liquid or
gaseous substances. There is no prospect yet of any general
comprehensive theory of catalysts. There is another group of
reactions in which the catalyst is in the same state as the substances upon which it acts. This is called "homogeneous catalysis." For example, an earlier process for making sulphuric

acid was the "lead chamber" process. In this the catalyst is a gas, nitrous anhydride, which is in the same state as the SO_2 and O_2 gases with which it is to act. And while we have a glimmering of the mechanism of "heterogeneous catalysis" in which solid catalysts cause reactions in the vapour phase, our understanding of "homogeneous catalysis" has hardly advanced at all.

This, it must be admitted, is a curious state of affairs. There is perhaps reason to hope that within the next twenty-five years or so a complete theory of the mechanisms of "heterogeneous," and of "homogeneous" catalysis as well, can be worked out. If this happens, it will then be possible to predict the appropriate catalyst to use for any particular type of reaction in industrial chemistry. Unfortunately, in spite of the great importance of this whole "chemical science within chemical science," in actual fact, during the last twenty-five years, although increased knowledge has in some measure helped to reduce the amount of research effort required to develop a new catalyst, nearly all the outstanding discoveries in catalysis have been empirical.

A schoolmaster teaching history nowadays takes care to avoid giving his pupils the impression that in centuries past people lived in savagery and squalor and made foolish decisions and were, in fact, not nearly as "advanced" as we are, and that, as the years went by, man progressed in wisdom and virtue. In science, on the other hand, there has undoubtedly been progress, but in describing modern science we must avoid giving the impression that we have reached perfection. The topic of catalysis is a striking example of the incompleteness of our knowledge. Not only do we make sulphuric acid and the other "chemicals" we are now about to discuss without understanding exactly how we do it, but the even more profound problem of the chemistry of life also depends on catalysts.

Superphosphate

Although much of applied chemistry in our modern life is devoted to industrial problems, that is the manufacture of materials, the chemist can never allow himself to forget that the world's supply of food is only just enough to go round. For that reason, almost a third of the large tonnage of sulphuric acid, the production of which we have just been discussing, is devoted to making fertilisers (Fig. 28). Plants are living things which, like ourselves, must "eat" to grow. One of the nutrient substances of which they find difficulty in getting enough is the element phosphorus. This occurs in considerable deposits in the southern and western United States and in Algeria and Tunisia. In its natural form it occurs as calcium phosphate, $Ca_3(PO_4)_2$. This salt, however, is not soluble in water so that

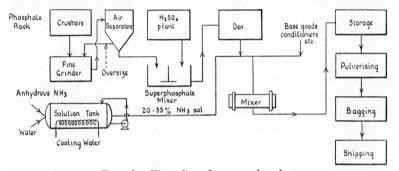

FIG. 28. Flow sheet for superphosphate
By permission from *The Chemical Process Industries*, 2nd ed., by R. N. Shreve. Copyright 1956. The McGraw-Hill Book Co.

plants can hardly obtain any phosphorus from it. But when it is treated with sulphuric acid it is converted into calcium acid phosphate which is soluble and from which crops can obtain their requirements of phosphorus. The reaction, written in its technical form, is:

$$Ca_3(PO_4)_2 + 2H_2SO_4 + 4H_2O \longrightarrow CaH_4(PO_4)_2 + 2(CaSO_4 \cdot 2H_2O)$$

Insoluble calcium phosphate — Soluble "superphosphate" — Gypsum

The simple chemical operation of making "superphosphate" fertiliser from the sulphuric acid, itself so simply made with the help of the almost incomprehensible (and therefore not yet fully scientific) process of catalysis, brings us to a second chemical achievement which also depends on a catalyst.

Nitrogen Fixation

The element nitrogen is a very common one. In fact, we are surrounded by it. More than three-quarters of the atmosphere is composed of nitrogen. In its elementary form, it is a comparatively stable and inert gas. Yet it takes part in at least two very important and practical chemical processes. In the sort of world we live in, its power of combining with oxygen to form nitrates or nitro-compounds is thought to be important for a nation's military strength. Saltpetre (potassium nitrate, KNO_3) is the oxygen carrier that provides the oxygen to combine with carbon and sulphur in gunpowder. The nitro-compound, trinitrotoluene, better known as T.N.T., contains three $—NO_2$ groups to supply oxygen to combine with the carbon skeleton of the toluene and make the whole molecule the powerful explosive it is. But beyond this compelling destructive and large-scale use of nitrogen it is also of vital significance in biology. The structure of all living tissues, whether of animals, plants or lower forms, depends on the peculiar chemical properties of the nitrogen atoms in them. The "living" part of living cells, that is the protein structure, the muscles that make animals move, growing cells, the enzymes in them that make the biological "engine" operate—all these depend on the nitrogen in their chemical structure. It follows, consequently, that besides phosphorus from superphosphate plants require a source of nitrogen so that they can grow into nitrogen-containing food for animals and for ourselves.

Elementary nitrogen—that is, the nitrogen gas of the atmosphere—is inert both to chemical reaction and for plants and animals. Nitrates, which contain the radical $—NO_3$, are sources of nitrogen for plant growth and are consequently valuable as fertilisers. Nitrogen, in somewhat the same way as carbon, has a versatile atomic structure that enables it to link with hydrogen as well as oxygen. Ammonia, NH_3, and ammonium salts are also like nitrates, easily available to plants for nourishment as well as being useful to chemists in many kinds of reaction.

Until about 1913 the world was kept going for its nitrogen

supplies as follows. Nitrogen in the atmosphere is "useless" for food or for chemists. Some of it, however, is converted to oxides of nitrogen by electrical discharges in the atmosphere. Although there is some doubt as to whether the nitrogen compounds in rain are increased in amount after thunderstorms, rain certainly contains traces of nitric acid (HNO_3) and nitrous acid (HNO_2). Indeed, it has been calculated that the world's supply of nitric acid increases by about 250,000 tons each day from this source. Another and a more important source of supply is the presence of certain strains of bacteria in soil and in the roots of some kinds of leguminous plants. From these sources crops obtain the necessary nitrogen for their growth, animals then eat them and are subsequently eaten by each other and by men. Eventually the men and animals die. Part of the nitrogen returns to the soil and part is lost. And so the "nitrogen cycle" recommences.

In some parts of the world there are stores of "banked" nitrogen just as there are depots of carbon, in the form of coal and oil, in other special areas. The biggest single deposit of nitrates is in Chile. This is an immense mass, 220 miles long by 2 miles wide by 5 feet thick. Nobody quite knows how the Chilean nitrate got there. Deposits of potassium nitrate are, however, found near cities in India, Persia and other oriental countries, and these are derived from the breakdown and oxidation of animal refuse by nitrifying bacteria. Similar theories have been postulated to explain the Chilean deposits.

Because, despite the "nitrogen cycle," there is a shortage of nitrogen for the growth of farm crops and for industrial uses for example, for explosives or the manufacture of nitric acid as an oxidising agent, Chilean nitrate was until 1913 an essential import for industrial countries. At that time Haber and a number of colleagues in Germany, working for the Badische Anilin and Sodafabrik, began to study seriously a rather obscure chemical reaction arising from the observation that when a "silent" electric discharge was passed through a mixture of nitrogen and hydrogen a very small amount of ammonia, NH_3, was formed. The equation for this reaction was:

$$N_2 + 3H_2 \rightleftharpoons 2NH_3 + 24,000 \text{ calories}$$

For a number of reasons, one of which was that ammonia, NH_3, cannot be completely decomposed by heat, several distinguished chemists of the time were sceptical as to whether the reaction shown in the equation really took place at all. Haber and his colleagues, however, forced the reaction to take place by doing two things. Firstly, reasoning that, if the formula were a true representation of events, *four* volumes of gas (namely one of nitrogen and three of hydrogen) were converted into *two* volumes of ammonia, they applied pressure to

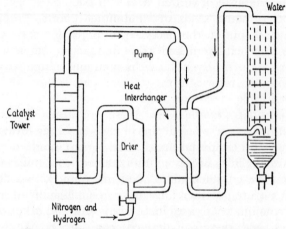

FIG. 29.   The Haber process for nitrogen fixation

the gas mixture, which was also heated to an appropriate temperature. As the pressure crept up from 10 to 50, to 100 and ultimately to 1,000 atmospheres, the proportion of ammonia produced grew larger. The second step taken by the German chemists was to find a catalyst. It seems rather odd, perhaps, but the best catalyst is made from pure iron! Small amounts of alumina and potash are mixed with it (Fig. 29).

So now we have an other immense chemical industry, with a capacity of more than 1,000,000 tons of ammonia a year, dependent on the ability of a catalyst to make a reluctant chemical reaction go. The industrial "fixation" of nitrogen, although a comparatively simple chemical reaction, is a complex engineering operation. First the gases have to be produced in the appropriate amounts. This is usually done by mixing air, steam and coke. This gives nitrogen and hydrogen, with carbon monoxide and carbon dioxide in addition. When the nitrogen and hydrogen have been sorted out, they must be compressed and purified by an elaborate system of equipment. Then at last, at a temperature of about 500° C. and a pressure of anything up to 1,000 atmospheres, the gas mixture is passed through a bed of catalyst. The ammonia produced is today the cheapest form of chemically accessible nitrogen available to industry and agriculture.

The principles of chemistry undoubtedly form a logical and coherent scheme of knowledge. Yet, until the fact had been discovered by Haber and his team in 1913, no one could have foretold that the manufacture of ammonia from air would depend on a catalyst of iron.

The Hydrogenation of Coal

The conversion of coal into oil is another example of chemistry of a highly practical nature made possible by catalysts. Although, as is only to be expected, coal has been subjected to a very large amount of chemical study, its exact composition even today is not fully understood. The broad relationship of coal quality to analytical composition is, of course, well known. Coal is principally composed of carbon, but though it is commonly thought of as a "mineral" it nevertheless carries with it, even after the lapse of geological ages, some of the complexities derived from its origin as living vegetable matter. Combined with the carbon, therefore, are hydrogen, oxygen and some nitrogen.

In 1913, Friedrich Bergius published a book on the work on high pressure in chemical actions which he had been doing in his own private laboratory in Hanover. From this he was led to examine the possibility of adding to coal more hydrogen than it naturally contained in order to produce a material with a chemical composition similar to that of petroleum. Eventually he succeeded in turning coal dust into oil and, appropriately enough, was awarded a Nobel Prize.

The Bergius process for combining hydrogen with carbon

(to make "petrol" out of coal) is in some ways similar to the
Haber process for combining hydrogen with nitrogen (to make
ammonia out of air). Sifted coal dust, mixed to a paste with
some of the oil already made, together with an appropriate
quantity of hydrogen gas, is pumped at a pressure of 200
atmospheres through a heater and thence into a series of pressure vessels. Once the combination of the hydrogen with the
carbon begins the reaction keeps itself hot. In about two hours

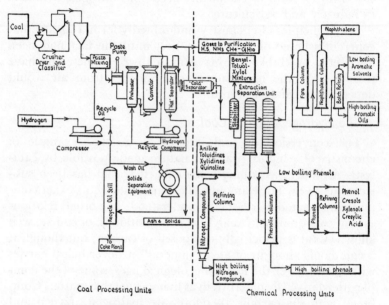

FIG. 30.   Chemicals produced by coal hydrogenation
Courtesy of *Union Carbide International Company.*

most of the coal has become converted into oil, "petroleum"
and fuel gas. However, none of these products would appear in
anything more than derisory amounts without the presence of
a catalyst (Fig. 30).

The catalyst found to be most effective in promoting the
combination of hydrogen with the carbon of coal to produce
"hydro-carbon" motor fuel is metallic tin. A number of other
materials, however, also act as catalysts for this chemical com-

bination. Metal oxides and sulphides are also active; carbonates and silicates "lubricate" the breakdown of the

$$-\overset{|}{\underset{|}{C}}-\overset{|}{\underset{|}{C}}-\overset{|}{\underset{|}{C}}-\overset{|}{\underset{|}{C}}-$$ linkage of coal to allow the combination of

the $-\overset{|}{\underset{|}{C}}-$ atoms with the H— hydrogen atoms. Unfortunately,

however, they not only facilitate the chemical changes leading towards the liquefaction of coal, they also favour the reverse reaction in which the already liquified dissolved coal turns back again into its original form of granular carbon. Tin does not give these undesirable backward reactions.

The Hydrogenation of Fats

Although liquid fuel derived from coal provides excellent high-grade motor spirit, its cost is usually greater than that of petroleum. There is, however, another application of hydrogenation, the discovery of which was a notable achievement and which is used to good effect on a large commercial scale. I refer to the "hardening" of oils.

Animal and vegetable *oils*, such as olive oil, linseed oil, castor oil and cod-liver oil on the one hand and the harder *fats*, lard, suet, blubber and the like on the other, are all members of the same chemical group. They are, in fact, mixtures of "fatty acid" compounds. These are composed of chains of carbon atoms of varying length from three or four (butyric acid in butter is four carbon-atoms long) up to eighteen or so. Carbon, it will be remembered, is an atom capable of linking up with four electrons. It has, as the chemist says, a valency of four. One important fatty acid is stearic acid with a structure thus:

$$\begin{array}{c} \text{H H H H H H H H H H H H H H H H H OH} \\ \text{| | | | | | | | | | | | | | | | | |} \\ \text{H—C—C—C—C—C—C—C—C—C—C—C—C—C—C—C—C—C—C=O} \\ \text{| | | | | | | | | | | | | | | | | |} \\ \text{H H H H H H H H H H H H H H H H H} \end{array}$$

(i.e. $C_{18}H_{36}O_2$)

There is, however, another common fatty acid, oleic acid, the
structure of which is

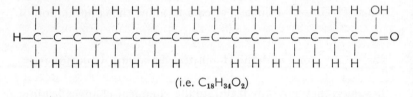

(i.e. $C_{18}H_{34}O_2$)

Now the main practical difference between fats and oils is
that fats come wrapped up in 1 lb. packets whereas oils are
found in bottles. To express this in more scientific terms, the
temperature at which fats melt is higher than that at which
oils melt. In the Arctic, both fats and oils are solid, whereas in
the frying-pan they are both liquid. And the main chemical
difference between them is that oils contain more oleic acid and
fats contain more stearic acid.

There is great demand in Great Britain, America and other
Western countries for solid fats—"hard" fats, as they are called.
Most of the cooking in these countries is done with lard-like
fats rather than with oil. Large quantities of non-liquid fats
are needed to make margarine. Indeed great commercial
development in the oils and fats industry followed the discovery of a process for converting liquid into solid fats.

It can be seen that the chemical operation required was the
addition of two atoms of hydrogen to the gap at the "double
bond" in the middle of the oleic acid molecule—in fact, *hydrogenation* once again. Up to the early years of the present century
many attempts had been made to do this, but the apparently
simple chemical operation proved in practice to be very
difficult. Quite elaborate processes were tried to fill the gap in
the molecule. Oleic acid was treated with sulphuric acid, or
heated under pressure with small quantities of iodine, or subjected to the action of hydrogen under the influence of a
"silent" electric discharge. None of these processes, however,
proved economically successful on a commercial scale. Eventually, the problem was solved by the application of what was
at the time a new observation—that hydrogen could be

assimilated by "unsaturated" compounds in the presence of a metallic catalyst.

The analytical techniques by which the composition and structure of the molecules of stearic and oleic acids were worked out can legitimately be claimed as part of our understanding of chemistry. They tell us *what* needs to be done to "harden" fats, namely to add hydrogen atoms. Even though we know now that fine turnings of metallic nickel will enable us to do the trick, yet the *way* in which the catalyst brings about the process of "reduction" by hydrogen is not yet completely understood.

The working of the process, now that it has been discovered, is not very complicated. Turnings of metallic nickel are placed in perforated cages in the reaction vessel and a stream of heated oil flows over them on one direction while a stream of hydrogen gas is pumped across the other way. The oil does not have to be excessively hot: a temperature of 140° to 200° C. is all that is needed. Although, as I have already said, the mechanism of the reaction caused by the nickel is not fully understood, it appears that the hydrogen links itself on to the fatty acids in stages. There are present, in fact, other "unsaturated" fatty acids than oleic acid, and some of these possess more than one double bond capable of accepting hydrogen. These more "unsaturated" acids appear to take up hydrogen first. The process can, therefore, be regulated and a greater or lesser degree of hardening brought about just as the operator wishes. This enables manufacturers of cooking fat to prepare a harder article for use in warm climates and a softer, less completely hydrogenated fat for cooler countries.

Other metals besides nickel can be used as catalysts to bring about hydrogenation, among them platinum and palladium. There are two objections, however, to their use. In the first place, they are expensive for a large-scale commercial operation; but more important is their tendency to become "poisoned."

The Poisoning of Catalysts

The "poisoning" of catalysts is a general phenomenon of much interest. The word is well chosen because the substances which block up a catalyst and prevent it from working act in precisely the same way as poisons that block the working of the biological chemistry of living cells. In fact, many of the same poisons that kill men also "kill" catalysts.

As I stated a little while back, solid catalysts act—so far as their mechanism is understood—either by presenting a very large surface area which forms a convenient platform for the reacting chemicals, or by a process of "chemisorption" in which the catalyst itself forms a temporary compound with one or other of the substances taking part in the reaction. This new compound is then better able to combine with the other constituent of the final reaction. The simplest process which occurs when a catalyst becomes "poisoned" and ineffective is that its surface pores get blocked up. Inert compounds may be deposited on the catalyst. Some of these "passive," or "temporary" poisons may be swept away if the subsequent stream flowing over the catalyst is not contaminated; but there are other types of chemical substances that are much more active in their poisoning effect. For example, sulphur is a particularly common and troublesome poison for many metallic catalysts. The reason is that it forms a chemical combination with the catalyst and thus prevents the "chemisorption" upon which the catalytic effect depends.

Cyanide is poisonous both to catalysts and to living creatures, and for the same reason. We have already mentioned that the energy for biological life is derived from the "combustion" of glucose, $C_6H_{12}O_6$, and its breakdown into $6CO_2$ and $6H_2O$ after combination with $6O_2$ from the air. Now outside the body glucose is a remarkably stable substance. The fact that we readily, continuously and at the comparatively moderate temperature of living tissues, obtain energy by the chemical combination of glucose and oxygen depends on a series of specialist catalysts. Biological catalysts are not primarily metallic, although certain of them contain metal atoms in their molecules. They are complex organic molecules called *enzymes*. Each one takes a separate part in passing hydrogen atoms out step by step from the glucose molecule:

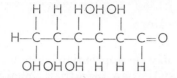

or alternatively in trapping oxygen and bringing it in so that gradually the ultimate combustion to $6CO_2$ and $6H_2O$ is completed. Certain important enzymes contain an atom of iron as a central structure of their molecules. The simple radical cyanide —$C\equiv N$ possesses a strong chemical affinity for iron, with which it forms a number of stable compounds. Prussian blue, for example, is a "ferrocyanide" compound. Other iron-cyanide combinations are also stable and strongly coloured. The chemistry of iron and cyanide interactions is interesting in itself, and its implications are far-reaching. It is because cyanide links itself so strongly and permanently to iron that it is so powerful a poison. By immobilising the iron in biological catalysts or, for that matter, in industrial catalysts, it destroys their ability to act. They become, indeed, "poisoned" in just the same way as living creatures are immediately poisoned by prussic acid (hydrogen cyanide), which destroys the catalytic properties of enzymes.

The fundamental importance of catalysts and catalysis is exemplified in a particularly striking way by our modern understanding of biological chemistry. The action of poisons like cyanide in killing us, not by stopping the chemistry of glucose combustion shown by the apparently simple equation $C_6H_{12}O_6 + 6O_2 \longrightarrow 6CO_2 + 6H_2O$, but by blocking the action of one of the catalysts that enable the chemistry to take place at all, shows in dramatic form how important catalysts are to the mechanisms of life. The examples that we have already discussed—the manufacture of sulphuric acid and the "fixation" of atmospheric nitrogen—indicate also the overwhelming significance of catalysts in industrial chemistry. It is, therefore, strange to realise how incomplete is our knowledge of the details of how catalysts work and our failure, in spite of a great deal of complex study and experimentation, to produce a fully satisfactory theory of catalytical activity.

Petroleum Cracking

Before turning to the somewhat more detailed topics of the next chapter, it may be appropriate to touch on one further application of catalysis to industrial chemistry from which great economic advances have accrued and which has fitted in a remarkable manner into the pattern of modern "automation."

Crude oil, when it comes to a petrol refinery, consists of a mixture of hydrocarbons (that is, compounds of hydrogen and carbon). The crude oil is pumped initially through a "heat exchanger" which heats it before it goes to the "primary" distillation column. The flow and temperature of the oil are automatically controlled by instruments. The "primary" column, which may consist of a large number of trays one above the other, is usually run under a partial vacuum, since this reduces the temperature needed to distil the oil fractions. The gasoline fraction, which vapourises fairly readily, is drawn off from the top of the column through a condenser in which it is cooled and reconverted to liquid petrol. Only about a fifth of the original crude oil is usually recoverable in this way direct as petrol. The fractions not distilled off through the first column pass to a second distillation stage. Different components are drawn off from this column at various levels. The least volatile material, heavy oil, comes off at the lowest level. The fraction above this is called "gas oil," above this again is kerosene or "paraffin oil," and higher up the column still is naphtha. These are cooled, condensed and collected separately. This whole set-up of two-stage distillation is nowadays run on a large scale and controlled almost completely automatically by temperature controllers, pressure controllers and flow controllers all automatically linked to run in harmony with each other.

As long ago as 1913 it was discovered that if the heavier (and less valuable) hydrocarbon fractions comprising the "gas oil" and paraffin streams were heated to something between 880° F. and 1000° F. at a pressure of anything from 100 to 500 lb. per sq. in., a chemical breakdown took place. Crude oil consists of hundreds of different hydrocarbons. In principle, what was achieved by this process of "thermal cracking" was the break-ing in half of some of the larger compounds, thus:

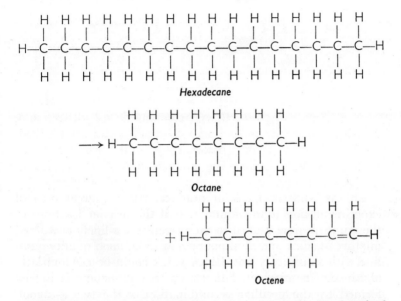

Hexadecane

Octane

Octene

Twenty-five years elapsed before the next step in the chemical control of petroleum production, the introduction of "catalytic cracking" processes. Thermal cracking usefully increased the amount of petrol produced from any particular amount of crude oil but it did not give petrol of the quality required for modern high-compression engines. In order to obtain adequate "knock rating" and at the same time to increase still further the output of the refinery, "cat cracking" was found to be essential. The operation is a highly successful application of modern science—it can increase the proportion of petrol obtained from crude oil from, say, 20 per cent. up to more than 50 per cent.—and involves the answers to two rather obscure questions. Firstly, how does the particular catalyst used do what it does? And secondly, exactly why does *iso-octane* so effectively control pre-ignition or "knock"?

The chemistry of iso-octane formation during catalytic cracking is as follows. The 8-carbon chain of octane breaks into two 4-carbon-atom pieces, and these pieces then link themselves together again in a different shape.

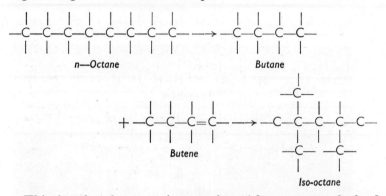

n—Octane   Butane

Butene   Iso-octane

This is what happens in practice. After a great deal of experimentation it was found that if the heavier fractions of the crude oil were heated in the presence of a finely powdered mixture of silica and alumina or magnesia, good quality gasoline with satisfactory anti-knock value could be economically obtained. Chemical analysis shows that iso-octane is indeed formed by the peculiar recombination of the two 4-carbon pieces of a "cracked" 8-carbon n-octane, but it does not exactly explain why the presence of this particular substance so effectively prevents pre-ignition in a high-compression internal-combustion engine.

The process of "cat cracking" (Fig. 31) is, of course, somewhat complicated. For example, the oil to be cracked needs to be heated until it is vapourised; it is then passed under pressure into a vessel, termed the reactor, together with the powdered catalyst which comes into the stream by gravity after having been regenerated from previous use. When the cracking reaction is complete, the catalyst is whirled out of the oil vapours in a machine called a "cyclone." The oil vapours then go into a distillation column to be separated into their various fractions and the catalyst falls into a hopper, from which it is blown into a regenerator by a stream of air in which the carboniferous materials which gradually settle on to it and which tend to clog its activity are burned off.

The control of this whole process is almost entirely automatic in a modern refinery. A large catalytic cracking plant may have from eighty to ninety controllers and from fifty to sixty recorders to balance pressures, temperatures, fluid and vapour

FIG. 31. The catalytic cracking plant at the British Petroleum Company's Kent Oil Refinery

flow, the amount of catalyst injected into the reaction column, etc.

Here then is an example of chemistry in action today, effective, precise and operating on a large scale under automatic controls. The product, high-grade petroleum, is essential to modern life and industry, which depends so much on the internal-combustion engine. And what makes the chemistry work in all the examples we have discussed in this chapter, and in more to come, is catalysis.

6

Carbon Chemistry

Carbon, as I have said before, is a very special chemical element. Its outer electron shell is capable either of giving or of receiving four electrons. That is, to use the technical vernacular, it possesses a valency of 4. In this, however, it is not unique. The special attribute of carbon is that, being either a giver or a receiver of electrons without prejudice, it is as ready to link itself to another carbon atom as to an atom of some other element. The result of this property of mutual linkage is that carbon atoms can link themselves into straight chains, branched chains, cross-linked series of chains like knitting, or folded and crinkled chains. It can, furthermore, join itself up into 4-, 5-, 6-, 7- or more membered circles, which in turn may be single circles or merged together like pieces of honey-comb as two, three, four or more rings sharing parts of their circumferences with each other.

The easy-going chemical nature of carbon implies that there are immense numbers of permutations and combinations—that is, enormous numbers of carbon compounds; both variations in the configuration of carbon atoms linked solely to other carbon atoms, and also compounds with other elements, such as oxygen, nitrogen, sulphur, phosphorus, and metals like iron, magnesium and zinc. The whole great topic of "organic chemistry" is, by definition, the chemistry of carbon compounds. By this definition it is clear that we must include within the ambit of organic chemistry not only biological chemistry, with the chemistry of animals and plants, their structure and the mechanism of their life processes, but also the chemistry of diamonds, coal, petroleum, textiles like cotton, wool and flax, and that of all the plastics, ranging from synthetic rubber to nylon and perspex.

In order to talk more easily about organic chemistry, that is, the chemistry of carbon compounds, it is first necessary to establish a few definitions. *Hydrocarbons* are, as their name implies, compounds solely of hydrogen and carbon. The simplest hydrocarbon is methane, which is the inflammable gas sometimes found in coal mines. Its formula is CH_4 and its structure is thus:

Methane belongs to the *paraffin series*, the next member of which is ethane, also a gas. Its formula is $CH_3 \cdot CH_3$ and its structure:

Then comes propane $CH_3 \cdot CH_2 \cdot CH_3$ and then butane $CH_3 \cdot CH_2 \cdot CH_2 \cdot CH_3$. All these compounds are gases; butane, however, is readily compressible to liquid and is marketed as a fuel called "calor gas." Butane leads us to another definition, that of *isomerism*. Two compounds are isomers when they have the same molecular formula but different structures and consequently different properties. The two isomers of butane are:

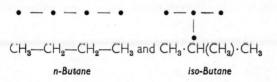

$CH_3{-}CH_2{-}CH_2{-}CH_3$ and $CH_3 \cdot CH(CH_3) \cdot CH_3$

n-Butane   *iso-Butane*

As organic molecules become larger and contain more carbon atoms, the possibilities for complexity and variety also increase. The member of the paraffin series next to butane is pentane C_5H_{12}. It possesses three isomeric forms. Thus:

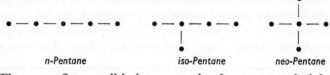

| n-Pentane | iso-Pentane | neo-Pentane |

There are five possible hexanes, nine heptanes and eighteen octanes—and so on in a steep geometrical progression.

Organic substances with open chains, including the paraffin series we have just described, are defined as *aliphatic* (or *acyclic*) *compounds*. When they contain a closed ring of carbon atoms they are defined as *cyclic compounds*. One of the most famous and characteristic of these latter is the aromatic substance benzene, derived from coal. Its formula is C_6H_6 and its structure is:

Benzene

Most petroleum products are paraffinic hydrocarbons. Open-chain hydrocarbons which are not fully saturated substances (with the formulae C_nH_{2n+2}) but contain an unsaturated linkage giving them the formulae C_nH_{2n}, are defined as *olefines*. The first member of the olefine series is ethylene, C_2H_4, the next propylene C_3H_6, the next butylene C_4H_8 and so on. The presence of a double bond, or unsaturated linkage, in ethylene makes it very much more chemically reactive than ethane.

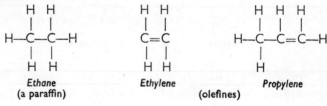

Ethane	Ethylene	Propylene
(a paraffin)		
	(olefines)	

Besides the division into groups such as *aliphatic* or *aromatic*, that is open-chained or ring compounds, organic substances are also classified according to their possession of certain special groups. For example, a substance is by definition an *alcohol* if it

contains the group —C—OH. In the series shown below,

ethyl alcohol is the compound which is the "alcohol" familiar to us as the intoxicating constituent of fermented drink.

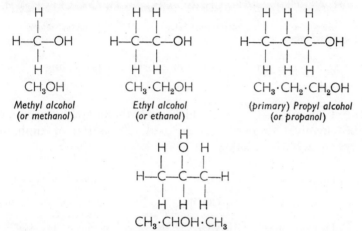

| Methyl alcohol
(or methanol) | Ethyl alcohol
(or ethanol) | (primary) Propyl alcohol
(or propanol) |

(secondary) Propyl alcohol

and so on.

If, instead of having an oxygen atom linked to one of its carbon atoms by a single bond, an organic compound has its oxygen linked directly by both its bonds to a carbon atom to which a hydrogen atom is also attached, it is defined as an *aldehyde*. The properties of the resulting series of substances are then different from alcohols and the formulae become:

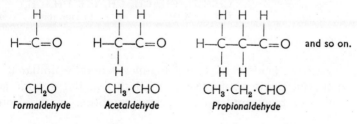

and so on.

Formaldehyde   Acetaldehyde   Propionaldehyde

A further variation is for a carbon atom *not* carrying a hydrogen atom to be doubly linked to an oxygen atom. Compounds with this grouping are called *ketones*. We thus find:

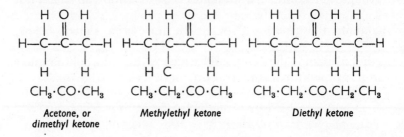

| Acetone, or dimethyl ketone | Methylethyl ketone | Diethyl ketone |

Organic acids are by definition substances possessing a "carboxyl" group,

$$\begin{array}{c} O \\ \| \\ \text{—C—OH}, \end{array}$$

which gives the organic compound the chemical properties of an acid. The series of aliphatic organic acids is as follows:

C_1 Formic acid	H·COOH	Liquid, boiling at 101° C.
C_2 Acetic acid	CH₃·COOH	Acid in vinegar, boiling at 118° C.
C_3 Propionic acid	CH₃·CH₂·COOH	Boiling at 141° C.
C_4 Butyric acid	CH₃·CH₂·CH₂·COOH	Predominant component of butter, boiling at 162° C.

.

.

.

| C_{18} Stearic acid | CH₃·CH₂·CH₂·CH₂·CH₂·CH₂·CH₂·CH₂· CH₂·CH₂·CH₂·CH₂·CH₂·CH₂·CH₂·CH₂· CH₂·COOH | Predominant component of suet, melting at 69° C. |

Organic acids behave in a manner generally similar to the inorganic acids we discussed in Chapter 3. But organic acids can also react under appropriate conditions with alcohols.

Although alcohols are not alkalis, the chemical reaction between acid and alcohol is not entirely different from that
between acid and alkali (on paper, at least!). For example, in
inorganic chemistry hydrochloric acid reacts with the alkali
sodium hydroxide (caustic soda), to produce sodium chloride
and water:

$$HCl + NaOH \longrightarrow NaCl + H_2O$$

The parallel organic reaction, which, however, requires
heat and is assisted by a catalyst as well, is for acetic acid and
ethyl alcohol to produce ethyl acetate and water:

$$CH_3 \cdot COOH + CH_3 \cdot CH_2OH \rightleftharpoons CH_3 \cdot COO \cdot CH_2CH_3 + H_2O$$

| Acetic | Ethyl | Ethyl acetate |
| acid | alcohol | |

This brings us to a further definition, that of an *ester*. An
ester is a compound formed between an organic acid and an
alcohol.

Besides the aliphatic alcohols and acids that have been so
far referred to, there are similar *aromatic* substances containing
ring groupings of carbon atoms in place of open chains. Among
common acids are:

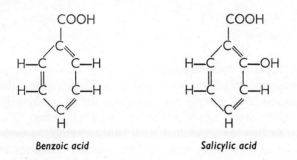

Benzoic acid   Salicylic acid

The first occurs naturally in many fruits and up to 0·1 per
cent. can be found in prunes or cranberries. Salicylic acid is
the principal component of oil of wintergreen. In chemical

combination with acetic acid, $CH_3 \cdot COOH$, it becomes acetyl-salicylic acid, which is "aspirin."

The simplest of the aromatic alcohols is benzyl alcohol, with the formula:

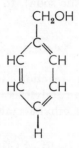

The possibilities of complex organic combinations are very great indeed. The benzene ring, first shown to exist as such in 1865 by Professor Kekulé at Ghent, was a fruitful interpretation applicable, as it was later found, to many other compounds. If we write the formula for benzene in a commonly accepted diagrammatic form, we can similarly indicate the structure of the other substances shown below:

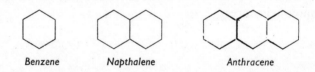

Benzene   *Napthalene*   *Anthracene*

The fact that carbon is so indifferent in its atomic behaviour and shows none of the predilections of those ionic substances that must either give or receive electrons in forming linkages with other atoms, means that as well as being able quite readily to link up in chains with other carbon atoms, it can also join as well with many other elements. Besides forming *homocyclic* rings composed solely of carbon atoms, it can also make up *heterocyclic* rings containing such elements as sulphur, nitrogen or oxygen as well as carbon. Usually atomic geometry is best satisfied by six-membered heterocyclic rings thus:

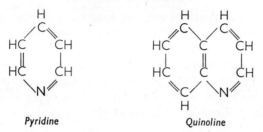

Pyridine   *Quinoline*

But five-membered rings are also quite common, thus:

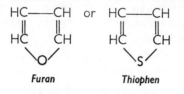

Furan   *Thiophen*

And rings of great complexity are possible and occur in nature. For example, camphor, which possesses the empirical formula $C_{10}H_{16}O$, has the structure:

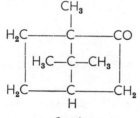

Camphor

Vitamin B_1 is even more complex in its heterocyclic structure; and very many substances with still more complex structures are known.

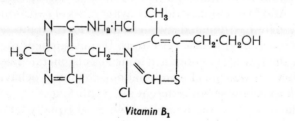

Vitamin B_1

Each of the types of organic substances we have been describing has its own special chemical characteristics. Alcohols as a group have properties which are different from those of aldehydes. And aldehydes are different from ketones, and so it goes on. Because of the possibilities of building carbon atoms together in diverse ways, many substances can possess more than one of these distinctive chemical groupings. For example, an organic molecule containing the group $-N\diagdown_H^H$ is defined as an *amine*. There exist in nature substances that possess both the $-NH_2$ amine group and the $-COOH$ carboxyl group. These are the so-called *amino acids* of which protein, the basic substance of living tissues, is composed. Amino acids are discussed in more detail later on (page 166).

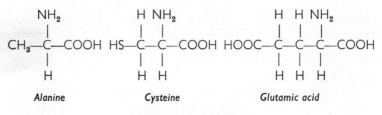

Alanine   Cysteine   Glutamic acid

(examples of amino acids)

When people begin to learn chemistry at school, they are first introduced to inorganic chemistry. Dalton's atomic theory leads naturally to a description of all the different types of elements that exist and to the laws that govern their behaviour. Among the first experiments the pupils do is the burning of magnesium to produce the new compound MgO, magnesium oxide. And magnesium oxide always consists of two atoms only, Mg^{++}, that has donated two electrons to combine with $O^=$ that has accepted the two electrons. It thus happens that when at last the learner has obtained some sort of general grasp of the principles of chemical combination, the new behaviour of carbon somehow seems different and confusing.

In fact, the laws of chemistry hold good equally for organic as for inorganic compounds. This understanding of organic chemistry, however, dates only from the end of the last century. Before then it was believed that some mysterious "life force" was required to produce organic substances.

The radical peculiarity of carbon, as we have said before, is that because it links so freely with itself and with other atoms, it can be used like a piece of mosaic stone, to build up an infinite variety of molecular patterns.

Vitamin B_1 is today manufactured by the ton as a fine chemical. It is used both in the United States and in Great Britain to enrich the nutritional value of white flour. The way in which the molecular architecture of this complex substance was discovered, and the process by which it subsequently became possible to manufacture it in a chemical factory makes up a good example of what organic chemistry is about and how it is handled in the practical world today.

As long ago as 1844 it was noticed by a shrewd observer called Takaki that the disease, beri-beri, which was a constant source of trouble because it reduced the effectiveness of the Japanese Navy, could be eradicated if the sailors' rations, which consisted largely of rice, were diversified and if a less highly refined grade of rice were issued. Although this showed quite clearly that rations had an important effect on health, the idea that some foods contain a particular chemical substance possessing a specific protective effect was not at that time grasped. About fifty years later, a Dutch medical officer, Eijkman, in the East Indies came nearer the truth. His servant kept hens which he fed on rice from the army stores. A new and more punctilious quartermaster was appointed who objected to "military" rice being used to feed "civilian" poultry, and Eijkman's servant was compelled to buy his own supplies. Shortly afterwards the birds developed polyneuritis, a disease which Eijkman had the insight to recognise as similar to the human affliction of beri-beri. He also discovered that a water decoction of rice polishings cured the hens and conceived the idea that the water had extracted a substance possessing therapeutic properties. Later this unknown hypothetical material was called vitamin B_1 (Fig. 32).

In another twenty years, that is by 1917, an American, Seidell, discovered that the active factor extracted from rice polishings could be concentrated one hundred-fold by adsorbing it on fuller's earth. Dutch, British and other American workers systematically tried all sorts of processes. The vitamin adsorbed on to the fuller's earth was, it was found, recovered again freed from some of its impurities by dilute alkali. More impurities could be precipitated by various chemical additions, for example by barium hydroxide or by silver nitrate. All this

Fig. 32.   A vitamin B_1 deficient pigeon and a healthy bird

time the chemical nature of the vitamin was quite obscure. The researchers merely tried one thing after another and tested the result on pigeons or rats to see where the active vitamin had got to. The research was, in fact, to a very large extent empirical. The sort of difficulty involved is shown by the fact that if the vitamin solution was made slightly acid, the addition of silver nitrate caused impurities to settle out leaving the vitamin in solution. On the other hand, if the solution were ever so slightly alkaline, silver nitrate caused the vitamin to settle out leaving impurities dissolved in the liquid!

After a long series of laborious separations, two Dutch

chemists eventually isolated a small amount of the vitamin in crystalline form. They analysed it to find out what elements it contained and discovered that its empirical formula was $C_{12}H_{18}ON_4SCl_2$. The unexpected presence of sulphur in the molecule agreed with the similar observation of a group of German workers.

The next stage in the historical process of chemical discovery came in 1934 and 1935. This was the determination of the structure of the substance, that is, how the twelve carbon atoms, the eighteen hydrogen atoms, the oxygen, the four nitrogen atoms and the sulphur were arranged. The knowledge was obtained in two ways: by diligent, painstaking and informed endeavour—and by two strokes of deserved good fortune. A team in the United States first observed that whereas the vitamin adsorbed on to fuller's earth could be removed by the *base* barium hydroxide, it could be removed much more efficiently by quinine sulphate, which is a "salt" of a base. This enabled them to prepare enough of the pure vitamin on which to do adequate analyses. In fact, they got about 5 grammes (something less than a fifth of an ounce) from a ton of rice polishings. The second stroke of good fortune was, however, even more delightfully unexpected. One week-end, wishing to preserve a solution of concentrated vitamin from becoming mouldy, they put into it from a handy bottle a little sodium sulphite as a preservative. When they came back on the Monday morning they found that a crystalline substance had formed on the bottom of the flask.

This substance was not the vitamin B_1 itself, but a substance $C_6H_9O_3S$. In fact, the action of the sodium sulphite had split the vitamin molecule in half. Although the two halves still required long-drawn-out and painstaking study before their nature was understood they were, of course, less complicated than the whole molecule. Eventually, the conclusion was reached that the nature of the crystalline substance so laboriously isolated from rice polishings was what is shown overleaf and that what sodium sulphite does is to divide it into two parts down the middle (incidentally, neither of the two half-substances possesses vitamin activity).

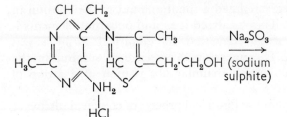

Vitamin B₁ (hydrochloride)

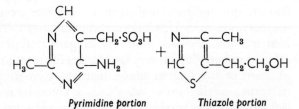

Pyrimidine portion   *Thiazole portion*

Before this feat of scientific identification could be accepted as the truth, the organic chemists had to set to work to build up the vitamin B₁ molecule from its elementary bricks. Only when the substance had been synthesised, according to the pattern deduced as I have briefly described above, and shown in fact to possess both the chemical and physical properties of the material derived from rice polishings and the biological activity as well, could the deduction be assumed to be a true bill.

This, of course, has been done. The pieces used in one method of synthesis are as follows:

Ethyl-ethoxy-propionate	$H_3C \cdot CH_2O \cdot CO \cdot CH_2 \cdot CH_2 \cdot O \cdot CH_2 \cdot CH_3$
Ethyl formate	$HCOO \cdot CH_2 \cdot CH_3$
Acetamidine	$H_2N \cdot C{=}NH$
	$\quad\quad\quad |$
	$\quad\quad\quad CH_3$

These, with appropriate manipulation with phosphorus-oxychloride and alcoholic ammonia, give the pyrimidine ring of the vitamin. When it is caused to react with a previously synthesised sulphur-containing piece called:

4-methyl-5-β-hydroxy-ethyl-thiazole

and the whole is treated with bromine and then with alcoholic silver chloride, the total structure of the naturally derived vitamin B_1 is obtained.

And this complex series of operations is today carried out in chemical factories which manufacture vitamin B_1 wholesale. This, and many other equally or more elaborate organic syntheses, is what fine organic chemistry does in the modern world.

This is not the sort of book in which it is appropriate to try to describe the technical methods by which organic chemists fit together one carbon atom with another and interlard carbon chains and rings with atoms of oxygen, nitrogen, sulphur or other elements. To do this would require a full-scale series of monographs. Today, organic chemists are prepared to attempt the synthesis of almost anything, although some substances present very formidable difficulties. Penicillin, for example, has been constructed synthetically in the laboratory but its manufacture was so difficult and expensive that it is, in practice, still produced by mould fermentation.

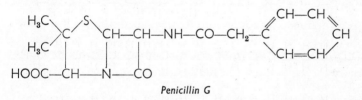

Penicillin G

As I have mentioned several times already, the special property of carbon as a chemical element is that carbon can be piled on carbon like one brick on another. But though bricks can be used to build an infinite number of forms depending only on the fancy of the architect, in fact, though one building may be different from another, most buildings do fall into one of a number of classes—for example dwelling houses, churches, blocks of flats and offices, town halls and factories—and it is generally possible to tell by looking at them to which class they belong. And the same thing holds good with organic substances.

Hydrocarbons we have already described. These, which vary in properties all the way from the four-carbon chain of butane, through chains of about ten carbons or so in petrol, and so on to longer chains in liquid paraffin, heavy lubricating oils and road-building tars and asphalts, are composed of carbon and hydrogen only. The edible vegetable and animal *oils* and *fats*, though like petroleum oils in some respects are different in others, particularly in the fact that they can be "saponified," that is, split into water-soluble "fatty acids," which we have already discussed, and glycerol. That is to say, these fats and oils are esters of the alcohol, glycerol and a series of organic "fatty acids." All normal fats and oils, ranging from liquid olive oil to solid lard or coconut oil, are similar in structure except that the harder fats contain the longer-chain saturated fatty acids. When fats are treated with alkalis they can be split into glycerol and soaps, which are merely the salts of the fatty acids. This is how soap (and glycerol) is produced industrially.

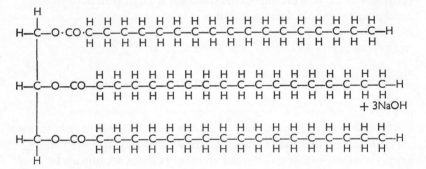

Fat (glyceryl tristrearate) + Sodium hydroxide (caustic soda)

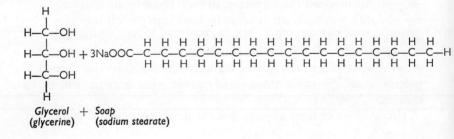

Glycerol + Soap
(glycerine) (sodium stearate)

The reason why soap gets rid of dirt is of some chemical interest. There are, of course, a number of different soaps (using the word in its chemical sense). They are, however, all formed by combination of a strong alkali, normally caustic soda NaOH, or caustic potash KOH, and a fatty acid. The alkali moiety of the soap molecule is strongly soluble in water. It is, indeed, described as "hydrophilic," or water-loving, whereas the long hydrocarbon chain, which is "lypophilic" or fat-loving is repulsed by water. When soap is mixed with water, the molecule tends to stand on end with its alkali "head" down under the surface and its fatty-acid tail up in the air. Greasy dirt becomes attached to the fat-loving end of the molecule and is thus dragged into the water by the more powerful water-loving end.

The modern artificial detergents use the same principle as soaps made from fats. In their manufacture, hydrocarbons derived from petroleum products are first converted into acids with sulphuric acid. These "sulphonated" hydrocarbons are then converted into sodium salts and are then often many times more effective as "wetting agents" for dirt and grease than traditional soaps. A characteristic formula would be:

$$Na \cdot SO_3 \cdot CH_2 \cdot CHOH \cdot CH_2 \cdot CH_2 \cdot CH_2 \cdot CH_2 \cdot CH_2 \cdot CH_2 \cdot CH_2 \cdot CH_2 \cdot CH_2 \cdot CH_3$$

Carbohydrates are another large group of organic compounds. Their name implies that they comprise carbon, hydrogen and oxygen. (The suffix "ate" carries the information about oxygen: for example, the nitrate radical is $—NO_3$, the carbonate $—CO_3$, the sulphate $—SO_4$ and so on.) The series of carbohydrates, in order of increasing complexity, is made up of simple sugars, of which glucose is the best known; disaccharides, or paired sugars, including sucrose—the "sugar" of everyday life; more complex substances comprising three or more linked sugar groups; then starches, which are big, conglomerate molecules of sugar units; and finally the most elaborate and rugged sugar combinations of all comprising cellulose, of which paper, cotton fibres and the like are examples.

The configuration of the simple *monosaccharides*, that is

carbohydrates made up of only one sugar unit, is like this:

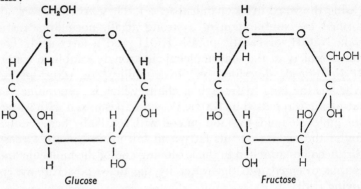

Glucose   Fructose

Two common *disaccharides* are sucrose and maltose (found in malted barley). These are shown below (the carbon atoms are written as • for simplicity).

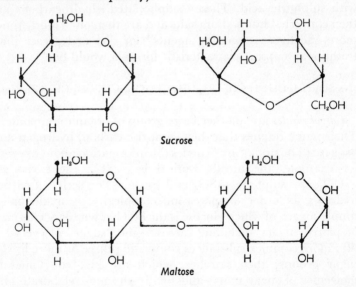

Sucrose

Maltose

Starch and cellulose are two *polysaccharides*. Their molecules consist of several hundred sugar groups linked together in this manner:

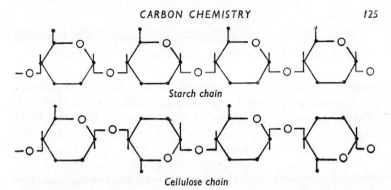

Starch chain

Cellulose chain

Cellulose is found in cotton fibres, flax, hemp, straw and wood. The chemical structure is a long chain of the six-carbon atom, so-called *hexose* units. An important principle of modern chemistry is that the atomic configuration shown above does actually exist and is reflected in the obvious physical properties of the substance, namely that it is a fibrous substance from which textiles or paper or the like can be made. The repeating structure is called a *polymer*. We shall discuss in a later chapter the synthesis of artificial polymers and the relationship of their physical properties to their chemical structure.

The starch linkage shown above is not so chemically resistant and tough as that of cellulose. It is for this reason that starch is digestible whereas cellulose is not. The nature of its molecule is also different. Although it is built up of hexose chains like cellulose, these are not all arranged lengthwise in fibres (though some of them are); certain starch fractions are composed of branched chains, thus:

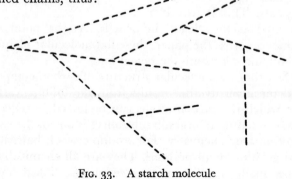

FIG. 33.   A starch molecule

This mixed-up configuration of the hexose chains in starch explains why it forms pastes rather than fibres like cellulose.

As we come to the end of this brief discussion of some of the main points of what is understood today as organic chemistry, it is important to stress the two things; firstly, that the structure of molecules that we show in diagrammatic form by their formulae really does exist in fact. And, secondly, this chemical structure is reflected in the physical properties of the substance itself.

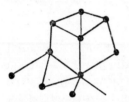

FIG. 34.   Carbon

Carbon in crystalline form, as diamond, is very hard because it is composed of atoms each linked firmly and directly to each other by four valency links. It consequently possesses a continuous pyramidal structure in three dimensions which has no weak points because every atom is linked to four other atoms (Fig. 34). In the case of graphite, however, which is also carbon in crystalline form, the atomic structure is arranged in two dimenions only (Fig. 35).

The picture as seen by X-rays confirms this structure and is shown in Fig. 36.

The atomic structure of graphite shows that its molecule is made up of layers of flat crystals. This is why it

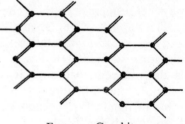

FIG. 35.   Graphite

can be used as the "lead" in pencils. As the point of the pencil moves across the paper, these flat molecular plaques are rubbed off and constitute the pencil line.

The fact that the molecular structure of carbon compounds, with all the diversity that results from the infinite variety of ways in which the carbon atoms can be linked, is reflected in the physical nature of organic substances is one of the cardinal points of organic chemistry. For example wool, hair, muscle, silk and gelatin are all proteins. They are all chemically large molecules made up of numerous *amino acids* linked together.

But the arrangement of the amino acids one with another is more varied than, for example, the arrangement of sugar groups in cellulose or starch. Wool, which is springy, possesses a "pleated" molecule. Silk has its amino acids linked in long

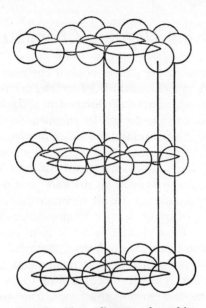

FIG. 36.   X-ray diagram of graphite

fibres. Gelatin, on the other hand, has its units arranged quite differently and not in a straight-line chain at all.

This chapter can only hope to describe in barest outline what organic chemistry is about. We can now try, perhaps, to say something of the use to which chemists are able to put their knowledge of it.

7

Using Organic Chemistry

The detailed knowledge which modern chemists possess of the workings of organic chemistry is, of course, put to practical use in making a great variety of things out of carbon. The two great sources of carbon for use in chemical factories are coal and oil. Although the atmosphere is full of carbon, it is for the most part in the oxidised form of CO_2, and energy needs to be put into it before it can be conveniently utilised. In actual fact, we allow ourselves to depend on the energy of the sun, geared into the CO_2 molecules of the air through the intermediacy of the chlorophyll of green leaves, to provide us with reduced carbon for food, for fuel, and as a chemical raw material. As I have mentioned before, the action of photosynthesis occurring in the green leaves of plants, was the process that originally enabled the stored reserves of coal and oil to be laid down.

One of the most important substances from which we make a great variety of the useful things we need in our modern, complicated industrial world is *phenol*, familiarly known in the household as "carbolic acid." Its chemical structure is:

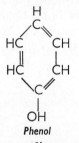

Phenol

This familiar substance was discovered more than a hundred years ago in 1834 by the German chemist, Runge, and was first brought to fame as an antiseptic by Joseph Lister, one of the fathers of modern surgical technique. From it are now manufactured great tonnages of plastics, a wide variety of dyes, numerous drugs, explosives, and disinfectants and soap, as well as a range of other chemicals.

Phenol, C_6H_5OH, comes in the first place from coal (and nowadays from oil), which is, as we have said, one of the big pools of carbon from which useful organic substances can be

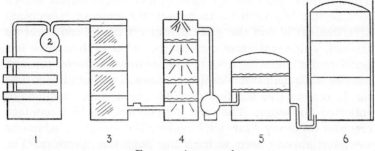

FIG. 37   A gas works

1. Firebrick retorts in which the coal is heated to 1,000–1,300°.
2. A wide iron pipe in which most of the tar collects.
3. A condenser and washer for cooling, condensing, and removing oils.
4. Scrubbers, in which ammonia, NH_3, is taken out of the coal gas by causing the gas to pass through water sprays.
5. "Purifiers", where hydrogen sulphide gas, H_2S, is absorbed by being passed through iron salts.
6. The coal gas ends up in the "gasometer", more correctly termed the "gas holder".

constructed. From the coal, as dug up out of its mine, the industrial chemist first makes tar. Coal varies a good deal in composition, according to its age, the geological stratum in which it occurs and several other factors. In general, tar is produced during the manufacture either of coal gas for cooking and heating or of coke for smelting. In principle, both processes are very similar and involve heating the coal in the virtual absence of air. Thus the carbon in the coal is not burnt (that is oxidised as in a fireplace) but is volatilised. In making coal gas, the coal may be put into horizontal vessels called retorts, each from about 10 to 20 ft. long, and heated to about 1,000° C. In modern gas works, vertical retorts are used. The operation of making coal gas out of coal is hardly a chemical process at all.

It is, rather, a simple separation of the coal into its components by heating it in the absence of air and then distilling it. A sketch of the operation is shown in Fig. 37.

Tar is also manufactured as a by-product when coke is made for smelting. This process differs from the production of coal gas in that the heating is arranged so that the volatile gas is decomposed and as much as possible of its carbon is left behind. This produces valuable amounts of ammonia and tar as well as gas, but less than in the gas-works process. The usual arrangement is that the gases driven off the heated coal pass through a pipe in the roof at about the centre of the oven into a water-sealed collecting trough, whence they are drawn through a series of air- and water-cooled condensers and scrubbers. The tar is removed in the first one. In the second, ammonia is collected in water. The first "scrubbers," which contain creosote or heavy "tar oil," collect the benzene, which as we have already seen is itself an important product. The

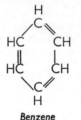

Benzene

remains of the coal gas, which by this time is a mixture consisting chiefly of hydrogen, H_2, and methane, CH_4, is returned to the coke ovens as fuel to heat the coal from which it came (Fig. 38).

Having extracted the tar from coal, by way of the manufacture of coke, either with or without the manufacture of coal gas, the chemist still has to get his phenol out of the tar. This operation is usually done by a specialised manufacturer called a "tar distiller," whose plant may be at some distance from the coke oven or gas works. There the tar is put into a still of some sort. If a "pot still" is used it may have a capacity of 3,000 to 8,000 gallons. The tar is boiled up in this vessel—a troublesome operation since it has a disagreeable tendency to froth. The first

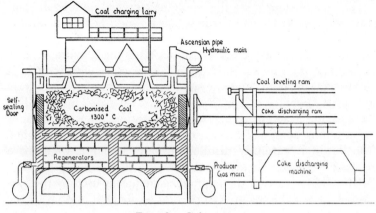

FIG. 38.   Coke ovens

fraction to distil over and be condensed is called "light oil."
This contains a comparatively small amount of benzene,
toluene and xylene. The reason why only a small amount is
recovered from tar is that most of this fraction has already been
collected at the coking plant. The composition of toluene and
xylene is shown below:

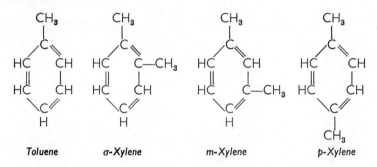

Toluene   σ-Xylene   m-Xylene   p-Xylene

When the "light oil" has all been boiled off the tar and
collected, the next fraction to be distilled off is called "middle
oil." This contains quite a complex mixture of organic substances which are called by the tar distillers "tar acids" and
"crude naphthalene oil," and is the fraction containing the
phenol.

The tar distiller takes the whole mixture of "middle oil" and stirs it up with water to which caustic soda has been added. Phenol is not called "carbolic acid" for nothing. It is, indeed, an acid and consequently combines with the alkaline caustic soda. The mixture of "middle oil" and water with soda in it is allowed to stand, and the soda-phenol compounds separate out as a lower layer which can be drawn off. This so-called "carbolate" fraction is then treated with just the right amount of sulphuric acid, which releases the phenol again. Then, when the liquid is carefully distilled, usually under a vacuum, a series of separate chemical substances are obtained for use.

It will be seen that the amount of chemistry used by the gas-works man or the coke-oven operator or, for that matter, by the tar distiller is not very great. Nevertheless, the amount of chemical understanding behind their operations is considerable, and the chemical knowledge originally needed to identify all their different products was very great indeed, as will be realised from this list of the substances obtained from the "middle oil" fraction of tar distillation:

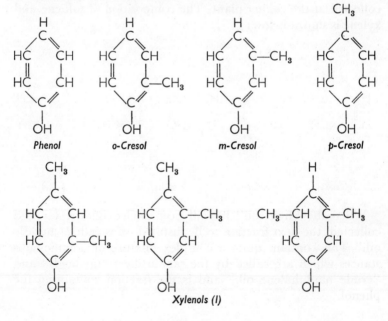

Phenol   o-Cresol   m-Cresol   p-Cresol

Xylenols (I)

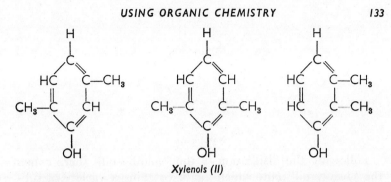

Xylenols (II)

Besides these, there are tar bases which are separated by being combined with sulphuric acid and subsequently "sprung" by treatment with alkali. They include pyridines,

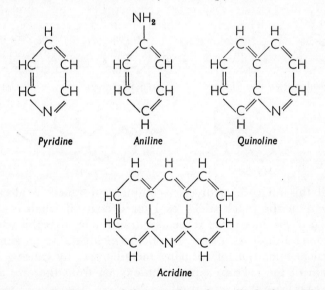

Pyridine   Aniline   Quinoline

Acridine

anilines, quinolines, acridines and various "substituted" compounds related to them. Finally, when all these have been taken out of the "middle oil," there remains naphthalene—commonly known for its use in "moth balls," but employed industrially for the manufacture of dyes, drugs, explosives, perfumes, disinfectants, photographic chemicals and much else.

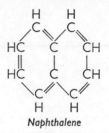

Naphthalene

Following the distillation of the "middle oil" there comes the "heavy oil" cut, which again contains a variety of substances which can be made to crystallise out as the hot distilled tar fraction is progressively chilled. This produces the following additional organic chemicals:

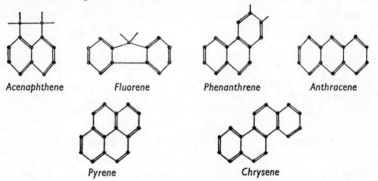

Acenaphthene   *Fluorene*   *Phenanthrene*   *Anthracene*

Pyrene   *Chrysene*

All this mixture of diverse, complex substances is already present in the black sticky coal tar driven off when coal is heated to produce coke. It seems extraordinary that this whole lot comes almost, as it were, as a bonus incidental to the simple chemical operation of reducing metallic ores by causing the carbon of the coke to sop up the oxygen from the ores and thus to release the metal itself.

(Burned in the blast furnace)   (becomes)
Coke + air ⟶ carbon monoxide + roasted iron ore ⟶ pig iron
                                                                              + carbon dioxide
$$2C + O_2 \longrightarrow \qquad 2CO \quad + \quad 2FeO \qquad \longrightarrow \quad 2Fe$$
$$+ \quad 2CO_2$$

And useful in all sorts of ways as these coal-tar components are, the simple phenol is probably the most important.

Phenol is of predominant importance for the following reasons. Firstly, it is today used in enormous quantities in the manufacture of Bakelite and many other plastics. We shall discuss the chemistry of these plastics in a later chapter. Secondly, it is used to make a large number of drugs, of which aspirin is the one that is consumed in the most substantial amounts.

Salicylic acid, used for medicinal purposes and as a preservative, was traditionally prepared from plants of the *Gaultheria* species (Fig.

FIG. 39. Wintergreen (*Gaultheria procumbens*)

39). A derivative is the main component of "oil of wintergreen." The structure of salicylic acid is:

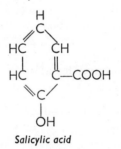

Salicylic acid

It is made nowadays by treating phenol with a strong caustic soda solution, drying the resultant product and treating it under heat and pressure with CO_2 gas. The sodium salicylate formed is reacted with an acid, which causes salicylic acid to be precipitated from the liquid. This is then converted into aspirin (acetyl-salicylic acid) by treatment with acetyl chloride, $CH_3 \cdot CO \cdot Cl$.

Between 1926 and 1935, the amount of phenol used in the

United States—taking that country as an example of modern chemical development—increased from 4,000 tons to 22,000 tons. By 1944, this amount had grown to 100,000 tons. The major part of this increase was due to the growth of the plastics industry.

So rapid an extension of demand outstripped the supply available directly from tar, and within recent years there has been a great industrial development devoted to the conversion of benzene, from the coke-oven gases, into phenol.

That is 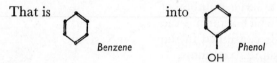 into

Benzene

Phenol

OH

The operation is a good example of organic chemistry in action. Although the change in the structure and composition of the molecule does not appear to be very great it has proved to be rather a troublesome one. In one process, the benzene is caused to react with concentrated sulphuric acid. The acid breaks into the benzene ring to produce benzene-sulphonic

acid When all the benzene has been "sulphonated,"

SO$_3$H

it is then heated strongly for about six hours in cast-iron vessels

with caustic soda. This produces the substance , the

ONa

sulphur moiety having been broken off as sodium sulphite, Na$_2$SO$_3$. A subsequent mild treatment with sulphuric acid

breaks off the sodium to leave free phenol which can be

OH

separated from the reaction mixture by distillation.

So here we have phenol—carbolic acid, if you like. It is a

constituent of tar, it is used in bakelite. It is needed to make aspirin and other drugs. Below is a further list of what it is used for in industrial processes built on to the knowledge of the principles of organic chemistry.

As a plastic   for adhesives
                            for protective coatings and paints
As a pharmaceutical   for salicylates, flavours.
For dyes
As chlorophenol   for bactericides and fungicides
For herbicides   the selective weed killers, "Verdone"
                            etc.
For photographic chemicals
For synthetic detergents
and for many other uses.

While we are discussing phenol and the benzene from which it is often made—both of these substances being got out of tar—it is worth while just touching on the chemistry of synthetic dyes. This topic is obviously too complicated to be dealt with in any detail in a book of this sort, but here is an example of what is done.

Dyes

First, the dyeworks chemist may construct the substance *anthraquinone*. He does this by buying some naphthalene from the tar-distiller and, by choosing a suitable catalyst (here once more catalysts!), oxidising it to phthalic anhydride, thus:

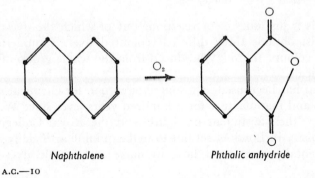

Naphthalene   Phthalic anhydride

A.C.—10

The phthalic anhydride is then caused, by appropriate chemical means, to combine with benzene from the gas works (or the tar distiller), and, in two stages, anthraquinone then appears thus:

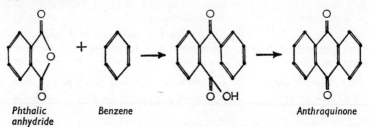

Phthalic anhydride   Benzene   Anthraquinone

Having acquired his anthraquinone, the dye-maker can then do all sorts of things with it. If he sulphonates it and then fuses it with a mixture of caustic soda and sodium nitrate he gets the dye *alizarine* (also called "turkey red"). If he then heats the alizarine with weak sulphuric acid he gets *purpurine* (a bluer shade of red). And if he heats this with strong sulphuric acid he gets a purple dye, romantically called *Alizarine bordeaux*. The reactions occurring are these:

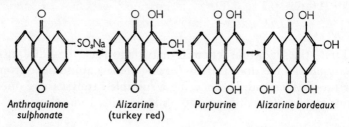

Anthraquinone   Alizarine   Purpurine   Alizarine bordeaux
sulphonate   (turkey red)

This is just one set of reactions out of which the dyestuffs chemist obtains three different coloured dyes. Innumerable other colours are today produced from the whole group of tar chemicals.

Coal has been used as a source of carbon for chemical synthesis and manufacture for a hundred years, ever since W. H. Perkin, then a student of eighteen at the Royal College of Chemistry in London, set out to make quinine artificially and accidentally discovered how to make a synthetic dyestuff, "mauveine," by oxidising toluidine from tar. Since then dyes, medicinal chemicals, perfumes, high explosives. disinfectants and other "fine chemicals" have been produced by the thousands from the same source of material. In 1879, from toluene, saccharin was produced—again quite by accident— and in 1939 from benzene there was derived D.D.T., that bids fair to exterminate one of man's oldest enemies, the louse. Here are their structures:

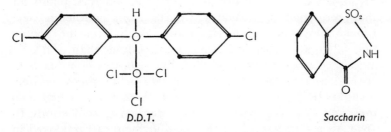

D.D.T.   Saccharin

But coal is expensive to dig and inconvenient to handle, and thus tends to be extravagant in manpower. It is, indeed, difficult to streamline and make automatic the processes of coal handling. Modern progress in industry tends increasingly towards "automation." But "automation" need not necessarily imply the introduction of more and more travelling belts in coal mines, or of automatic froth-suppressors in the tar-distilling works. A more fundamental application of the new principles of automatic technology is the substitution of a more amenable source of chemical raw material. And that, in fact, has been done.

Petroleum Chemicals

The winning of petroleum, its transport by simple pumping from remote "mines" to ships and thence to refineries, and the quite complex problems of purifying and classifying the various streams intermixed in the original crude oil, are handled with infinitely less demand for human labour than the handling of an equivalent amount of coal. Petroleum, which when chemically combined with oxygen (that is, combusted) can give us fuel and motive power so much more conveniently and with so must less demand for human labour than coal, can also supply almost every kind of organic chemical in the same streamlined manner.

Organic chemistry—that is the chemistry of carbon compounds—is, as we have seen, so fundamental to modern life, with its drugs and explosives and insecticides and its plastics of all sorts, from artificial rubber to nylon carpet brushes, that it s important to realise the suddenness and completeness of the revolution that has occurred. The first commercial plants for the production of carbon chemicals from petroleum were brought into action in America in 1930. At that time the production of organic chemicals from sources other than coal only amounted to about 300,000 tons. By 1936, this figure had increased to 1,000,000 tons, the increase being almost entirely due to petroleum chemicals. By 1941, the figure was 2,500,000 tons, and by 1944 it had reached more than 5,250,000 tons. In 1952, three-quarters of all the organic chemicals produced in the United States were derived from petroleum.

Just as crude coal can be distilled to separate from it the tar and the other fractions that we have been discussing, each of which contains the long list of diverse substances waiting to be sorted out and used, so crude oils contain substantial amounts of benzene, toluene and the xylenes and much else. Furthermore, as petroleum is made up of a mixture of paraffins and olefines of varying carbon-chain length, it is no serious problem for the organic chemist to convert these—by catalytic as well as by purely "chemical" methods—into such industrially useful substances as

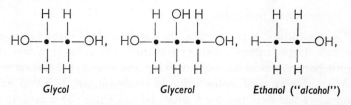

Glycol   Glycerol   Ethanol ("alcohol")

and many others. Ethanol, familarly known as "alcohol," when passed in the form of vapour over a suitably heated catalyst, reacts to form butadiene, which can be used in the large-scale manufacture of artificial rubber. The reaction is as follows:

$$2CH_3 \cdot CH_2OH \longrightarrow CH_2 : CH \cdot CH : CH_2 + 2H_2O + H_2$$

Ethanol $\qquad$ Butadiene

From what we have seen of the structure of organic chemicals it is clear that there are few of the main carbon compounds used by modernindustry that could not theoretically be built up

using methane, $H—\overset{\displaystyle H}{\underset{\displaystyle H}{|}}—H$, as the basic unit. This is obviously

the most completely reduced form in which carbon can occur and its combination with other atoms would tend to release energy rather than require it. Three possible sources, coal, petroleum or vegetable material such as sugar, starch or cellulose, could be used to provide this CH_4 carbon. But petroleum possesses two substantial advantages as a source of methane. The first is that it is already a combination of carbon and hydrogen, which is a help to the organic chemist, and the second is, as I have remarked, that it lends itself so readily to being handled by the modern automatic processes. For this reason the enormous and sudden development of a petro-chemical industry is of peculiar significance.

But petroleum is not only a potential source of very many organic chemicals. It is already an actual source of important materials. Industrial alcohol (ethanol) derived from petroleum hydrocarbons has already been referred to. Formaldehyde, $H—\overset{\displaystyle C=O}{\underset{\displaystyle H}{|}}$, a basic organic chemical in numerous processes, which is used in the manufacture of plastics in combination with phenol, and also in textiles, drugs, leather processing and much else, is made nowadays from petroleum. The formaldehyde can be produced by the catalytical reduction of methanol by red-hot platinum. Acetic acid, which is of great importance in the production of cellulose acetate textiles (Rayon); acetone, $CH_3 \cdot CO \cdot CH_3$, otherwise produced by fermentation; acetylene $HC{\equiv}CH$, previously made by the reaction of calcium carbide and water; isopropyl alcohol, $CH_3 \cdot CHOH \cdot CH_3$, which is a versatile solvent; glycerol, which we have already mentioned, and which is a key constituent of many explosives (for example, nitroglycerine); these and very many more chemical products are today being manufactured on a large scale from petroleum.

But although the organic chemist today possesses the knowledge that enables him to put together simple pieces of a molecule—for example, methane CH_4—to make a complex whole, in actual practice he, like the rest of us, prefers to obtain the substances he wants ready-made. For example, sucrose, the everyday "sugar" of the dining-room table is, in the form in which we eat it, a pure crystalline chemical with the structure shown below:

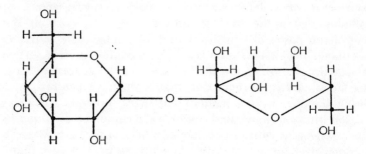

As we well know, the thousands of tons of sugar that are "manufactured" each year are not synthesised from the carbon of coal tar, or, for that matter, from carbon fractions broken off the hydrocarbon chains of petroleum. They are extracted ready-made from the stalks of sugar cane or from the roots of sugar beet. The operation, although it is now carried out in large factories as everyday routine, is based firmly on the understanding of the chemical nature of sucrose. It is worth remembering that although the sweetness of sugar has made it a material in strong demand through much of history, its production in bulk had to await the advent of the chemical technology of the nineteenth century.

The operation of sugar manufacture is done like this. First, the juice of whatever plant is used as the raw material is extracted. With cane, this is done by crushing the stalks between heavy rollers. The crushed cane is later washed with hot water. Sugar is removed from beet by slicing the roots into small strips and extracting the sugar with hot water in a machine sometimes called a "diffusion battery." Both these processes, of course, take advantage of one of the properties of sucrose, namely, its solubility in water. Nevertheless, all sorts of other components of cane and beet also dissolve in water and only by the exercise of chemical knowledge can they be separated from the sugar.

The first use of chemistry is to neutralise the acidity of the juice. This is necessary because the sugar molecule splits in half at the central link if it is subjected to heat in an acid medium. Thus, while the sugar manufacturer might end up with the two halves, namely, glucose and fructose, these are not "sugar," in the housewife's understanding of the term—for one thing the mixture is less sweet. The alkali used is quicklime and water, which combine to form calcium hydroxide, $CaO + H_2O \longrightarrow Ca(OH)_2$.

When the acid has been neutralised, the juice is boiled. This can now safely be done without destroying the sugar molecule. The heat, however, "denatures" the large protein molecules present as impurities. The chemical effect is similar to the change that takes place in egg white when an egg is hard boiled. The juice is now separated from this first lot of unwanted impurities and may then be treated with sulphur dioxide gas. This again has no effect on the sugar itself but the sulphur dioxide reacts chemically with the residual lime and produces a new sediment of calcium sulphite which, in falling through the liquid as a granular precipitate, draws down other impurities in the juice in somewhat the same way as rain cleans impurities from the atmosphere. The reaction between the sulphur dioxide and the calcium oxide is as follows:

$$CaO + SO_2 \longrightarrow CaSO_3$$

After the sugar has thus been extracted from the cane or beet in which it has been synthesised biochemically by the plant,

and after it has been separated from the main impurities as we
have just described, it must next be made to crystallise from
the water in which it is dissolved. This process of *crystallisation*
is used throughout chemistry as one of the basic operations for
separating pure substances. The sugar manufacturer starts by
removing about 70 per cent. of the water in an elaborate plant
called a "multiple-effect evaporator." The syrup so formed is
boiled up again in a "vacuum pan." The vacuum allows the
operator to boil the syrup at a lower temperature than would
otherwise be possible and thus avoids "burning" it, as the
housewife would say. Eventually, the sucrose crystallises out
and can be removed in a centrifugal machine somewhat similar
to those often used domestically for drying clothes after they
have been washed in a washing machine.

Even though much of the remaining impurities still mingled
with the sugar remain in the black molasses left after the sugar
crystals have been centrifuged out, these crystals themselves
still require further purification. In modern refining processes,
the sugar crystals are first washed with a small amount of water
to remove adhering molasses. Next, the sugar is dissolved in
sufficient water to form a syrup and is filtered through a cloth.
The syrup is then passed through a filter made of "bone char"—
charcoal made from bones. The use of this material dates back
to 1830, when the process was patented. The bone char absorbs
impurities, that is traces of substances giving colour to the sugar
crystals. It has an important advantage in that, after it has been
used, it can be roasted and is then ready for the treatment of
another batch of syrup. After the bone-char "bleaching," the
syrup is boiled again and the sugar, now substantially pure
sucrose, allowed to crystallise.

Here then we have described two kinds of ways in which
organic chemistry is used in practice. Behind both is the considerable corpus of scientific knowledge—knowledge of atomic
structure, molecular configuration, valency bonds, and the
like. But though the principles of organic chemistry are complex and long to learn, the practice is often simple. To prepare
sugar, the involved molecular structure of which was shown on
p. 142, one merely discovers where it is to be found—in beet or

in cane or, for that matter in other plants (cane is, after all, only an overgrown variety of grass). And having decided on a source, one goes through what on the surface appears to be an art, rather than a science, of liming, and boiling, and sulphiting, and treating with—of all improbable materials—charred bone.

But then the operations of tar distilling do not seem at first sight to be so very "chemical" either. The great dirty pots, and the frothing tar, the distillation columns, the smell. . . . Nevertheless, there are in the tar, come out of the coal after its heating without air, all the long list of phenols, and cresols, and xylols; the pyridines, and the anilines, the naphthalene, and the anthracene and many others, some of which are shown diagrammatically in the earlier pages of this chapter.

There is some degree of paradox in the contrast between the complexity of the chemical structure of these substances and the simplicity of many of the operations that are carried out in using them. This paradox, however, is not peculiar to industrial organic chemistry. The mechanism of the nervous and muscular control needed to run across a court and, while still running, hit a moving tennis ball is complicated in the extreme. Even the control of one's eyes to keep the moving ball in focus from the position of a by no means steady head is a feat calculated to puzzle the best expert on gyro-controlled gun turrets for battleships. And yet we do it without a thought.

Organic chemistry, in practice, is made up of two kinds of operations. There is on the one hand the more or less straightforward *separation* of useful substances from the mixtures in which they occur in their crude "ores." The separation of pure sucrose, that is table sugar, from sugar beet or sugar cane is one example. The isolation of industrial alcohol by distillation from the mixed compounds derived from the fermentation of molasses by yeast is another. We shall be discussing this further in Chapter 8. But the most striking examples of industrial organic chemistry separating substances of useful molecular configuration from mixtures are the isolation of all the numerous substances from coal and, increasingly in modern times, from crude oil.

The second kind of industrial organic chemistry is much

more "chemical." The manufacture of aspirin, for example, requires—as was stated earlier on—the reaction of phenol with caustic soda, the heating of the product under pressure with carbon dioxide, the reaction of this product with acid, the collection of the precipitate from the reaction and its treatment with acetyl chloride. There are enormous numbers of operations of this type, based on an extensive and detailed knowledge of organic chemistry, by which all manner of useful substances are made. Vitamin C, for example, the active vitamin in orange and lemon juice, is nowadays synthesised in factories in large amounts. The progression of events is a complicated one. A sugar, l-sorbose, is reacted with acetone, the resulting compound extracted with ether, oxidised with permanganate, and the substance thus produced heated under acid conditions. The starting material, l-sorbose, has the following structure:

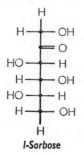

l-Sorbose

The ultimate product required, namely vitamin C, has this structure:

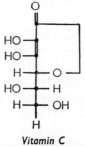

Vitamin C

The various steps achieved in passing from the initial starting

material to the ultimate vitamin require a very high degree of
chemical virtuosity. Here they are:

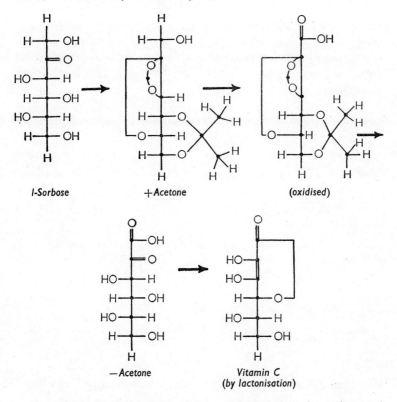

l-Sorbose   +Acetone   (oxidised)

—Acetone   Vitamin C
                (by lactonisation)

But although we cannot fail to admire the virtuosity and
resource of the organic chemists who are able to elaborate a
method such as this in order to manufacture vitamin C by the
ton, it is important to notice one thing. This is that the whole
business starts with the sugar, l-sorbose. And l-sorbose is not
a particularly common substance. In fact, in order to get it at
all the chemist must either go to the mountain ash, *Sorbus
aucuparia*, for berries, which is hardly a practicable proposition
on the factory scale, or else he must depend on living bacteria
to synthesise the sorbose. This, in fact, is the way it is obtained.

The point I want to make is this. Organic chemists can, by

the knowledge of their science that is now available, synthesise very many substances. In practice, however, they usually achieve their results by using prefabricated sections of the substances they are aiming to make. These sections they obtain ready-made from tar or from petroleum or, perhaps, from a biological source. At this point, therefore, it is appropriate to turn our attention to the chemistry of biology, that is, of living organisms.

8

Biochemistry

It is only during the last hundred and fifty years that it has been fully realised that living organisms are composed of substances which can be studied chemically just like any other materials, and that the functions of living and the energy of life are manifestations of chemical energy. The combination of carbon with oxygen is, as we have already seen, the commonest source of energy on earth, whether it is used as combustion, either to produce heat and hence steam for locomotives or electric power stations or to drive machines like internal-combustion engines, or whether it is used to provide the chemical energy needed to reduce metallic ores by smelting. It is this same release of chemical energy from the oxidation of carbon that gives animals the power to live.

Right into the nineteenth century people thought of living creatures and the stuff of which they are made as something different from chemical compounds. The chemistry of living things seemed so different from the simple chemistry of acids and salts that it was doubted whether it could be described by the same laws that were being discovered in the laboratory, and many workers thought that a special "vital force" entered into the making of the fat, sugar, protein and many other compounds that are only found in living things. The German chemist, Wöhler, who in 1828 prepared urea—a characteristic example of a typically animal product—seemed, however, to settle the matter. Actually, Wöhler's proof was wrong although his conclusions were right.

The foundations of our present understanding of the remarkable nature of biochemical processes were, however, established by Lavoisier and Laplace in 1789. The purport of their investigations was that when an animal breathes, oxygen is absorbed, carbon dioxide is given off and heat is produced. They measured with considerable accuracy the relative amounts of CO_2, O_2 and heat involved and concluded, quite correctly, that "respiration is a process of combustion which, though it takes place very slowly, is perfectly analogous to that of the combustion of coal."

The first experiments were done with guinea pigs. From these Lavoisier and his collaborators conceived the idea that animal

Fig. 40.   Lavoisier's experiment with Seguim

heat is derived from oxidation, that the same oxidative process, in fact, goes on in the body as in a fire. Next, experiments were made on one of these collaborators, a young M. Seguim, shown in the illustration (Fig. 40). Seguim is shown doing a measured amount of work with one foot. Some excellent experiments were carried out which showed that more food—as fuel—had to be used when work was being done and which measured exactly how much more. On the basis of this experimentation, Lavoisier concluded that "La vie est une fonction chimique," or in English, "Life is a chemical process."

It is now quite clear that there is no such thing as a special "vital force" peculiar to living organisms. Whatever a living cell does has to be paid for in the currency of chemical energy. If there is no free energy available there is no life. The animal does not generate its own energy but obtains it from the chemical molecules of its foodstuffs. And the cell knows two methods of getting out the energy of these fuel molecules: it either fragments them or burns them. The second method is going on in the sort of process observed by Lavoisier, namely in the process of respiration. The chemical operation is as follows:

$$C_6H_{12}O_6 + 6O_2 \longrightarrow 6CO_2 + 6H_2O$$
Sugar (glucose)   Carbon dioxide + water

The first process, that of fractionation, is best exemplified by one of the ways the living yeast organism gets energy out of sugar, that is by *fermentation*. The net chemistry of this operation was established by another French chemist, Gay-Lussac, in 1815, thus:

$$C_6H_{12}O_6 \longrightarrow 2CO_2 + 2C_2H_5OH$$
Sugar (glucose)   Carbon dioxide + alcohol

These two ways by which the living body obtains energy seem on the face of them to be remarkably simple chemistry. The equations look quite straightforward. Glucose ("blood sugar," as the doctors call it) circulates through the pervasive arteries and capillaries to all the diverse cells of the body in rather the same say that petrol is carried through pipes from the fuel tank to the cylinders of a motor-car or aeroplane engine. But in fact the chemistry is not simple. There are, indeed, many quite competent industrial chemists who need to be told this: biochemistry, although part of chemistry, has its special limiting conditions and operates through certain peculiar channels which make it quite distinct from the other branches of chemistry. For example, although in respiration $C_6H_{12}O_6$ breaks down into $6CO_2$ and $6H_2O$ and releases a lot of chemical energy, and although in the process of fermentation the same $C_6H_{12}O_6$ splits up into $2CO_2$ and $2C_2H_5OH$ and releases part of its chemical energy, yet no matter how long glucose (that is $C_6H_{12}O_6$) is left in the laboratory at the temperature of a living body it will never undergo either of these reactions.

The first answer to this apparent enigma is—catalysis. And the second and more precise answer is that the catalytic effects occurring in living tissues are not single reactions such as occur when metallic catalysts are used in, say, "cat crackers" or in "fixing" atmospheric nitrogen. The catalytic reactions of life are brought about by a whole series of graded organic catalysts called *enzymes*.

The precise mode of action of enzymes is not completely understood. They appear, however, to be complex compounds of a protein structure (that is constructed of *amino acid* units), each containing a specific chemical configuration analogous to the indentations of a lock into which fits one particular key. The converse structure to the pattern of the indentations is the part of the molecule (glucose in the case of glucose breakdown) which is broken off at each stage of the process of respiration or fermentation. The delicacy of this chemical structure is disturbed by heat as well as by a variety of poisons, some of which effect one enzyme only and some many.

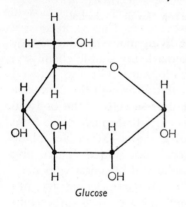

Glucose

The complexity of the apparently simple Gay-Lussac equation of 1815 was finally shown as what it is—a series of gradual steps each dependent on a specific organic catalyst—only in 1947. The series of changes involved are as follows.

A first enzyme causes the glucose from which the whole operation starts to combine with a phosphate radical
$$-O-\overset{\displaystyle\overset{O}{\|}}{\underset{\displaystyle\underset{OH}{\diagdown}}{P}}-OH;$$
indeed in the absence of phosphate the biological process of fermentation cannot take

place at all. The glucose-phosphate ester, as it is called, is then sprung across into a fructose-phosphate ester by a second enzyme, thus:

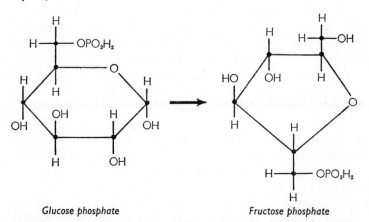

Glucose phosphate   *Fructose phosphate*

Another enzyme causes a second phosphate radical to combine to produce a substance which in honour of its discoverers is called the "Harden-Young ester." Yet another enzyme splits this from a 6-carbon substance into two 3-carbon substances. A further phosphate radical becomes linked on to form a key glycerol derivative *di-phosphate*.

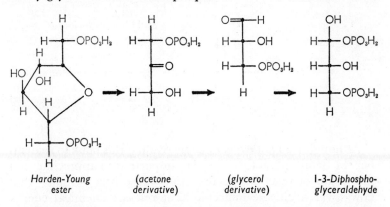

| *Harden-Young ester* | *(acetone derivative)* | *(glycerol derivative)* | *1-3-Diphospho-glyceraldehyde* |

The substance, 1-3-diphospho-glyceraldehyde, is important to the whole operation because under the influence of a special complex compound, *co-zymase*, which acts as a kind of chemical "pump," it becomes oxidised and by this fact causes the substance six stages further on to become reduced. This substance is acetaldehyde

and its reduction product is alcohol

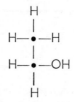

The chain of compounds between 1-3-diphospho-glyceraldehyde and alcohol is as follows:

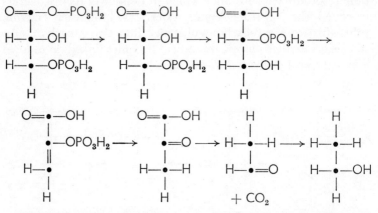

Although I do not expect people reading this book to remember the details of all this, it is very important to appreciate that this chain of reactions occurs—thus there is a "ripple" that flows over a glucose molecule as it releases chemical energy for the use of the living yeast, or whatever other creature (and there are many) uses the method.

Knowledge of this chemistry in the living cell is of practical importance in at least two ways. Firstly, it is used in medicine and physiology. For example, it is now known that one fragment of the enzyme system that carries the last part of the "ripple" from pyruvic acid

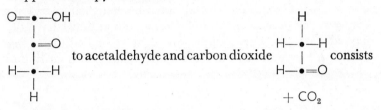

to acetaldehyde and carbon dioxide   consists

of the chemical substance vitamin B_1. Consequently, it is now understood that the disease beri-beri, which is due to an inadequate supply of vitamin B_1 in the diet, is associated with an accumulation of pyruvic acid in the blood stream (Fig. 41). The second practical implication of a knowledge of the complexities of biochemical reactions is that it enables us to some degree to command the situation. An example is provided by a method for the commercial manufacture of glycerol for explosives. This is achieved by putting sulphite into a fermenting sugar solution. Sulphite and acetaldehyde combine and the acetaldehyde is, therefore, not available to be reduced. Consequently, the 1-3-diphosphoglyceraldehyde further back along the system does not get

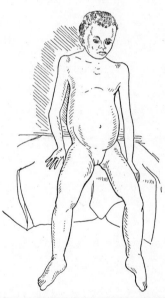

Fig. 41.   Oedematous beriberi with paresis of legs

oxidised and the process of fermentation becomes stuck at this point and eventually glycerol accumulates and can be separated for use.

The comparative simplicity of micro-organisms has made it easier for scientific workers to study the chemistry by which these creatures release energy by gradually and partially oxidising carbon-containing fuels such as sugars, which for most of them as well as for us higher animals are what keeps the process of life going. Not all microbes get their energy for living by the process of alcoholic fermentation that I have described for yeast. For example, an organism called *Clostridium acetobutylicium* found in soil does not split sugar primarily into

the 2-carbon atom fractions of alcohol 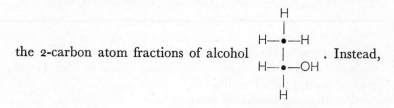 . Instead,

it fractionates the 6-carbon sugar molecule into butanol

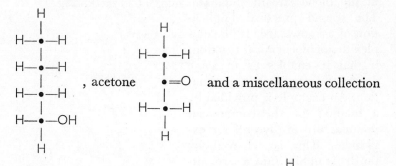 , acetone   and a miscellaneous collection

of other substances, including acetic acid   , hydrogen

and CO_2. Since this remarkable biochemical behaviour of *Clostridium acetobutylicium* was first observed by Louis Pasteur in 1861, a great deal of work has been put into studying how the reaction is achieved, and a chain of inter-related, catalytically induced chemical changes could now be written down as we did for yeast a page or so back. The result of this effort is to be seen in the large factories in Great Britain, the United States, Canada and elsewhere which can produce thousands of tons of acetone (a solvent in cordite manufacture) and butanol (an intermediary in synthetic rubber production) and which depend on the specialised biochemistry of this particular microbe.

Penicillin is a more remarkable example of the advantage taken of unusual chemical reactions brought about by living cells. The group of *Penicillium* moulds is not so very far removed along the biological tree from the yeast which we have already discussed. And, incidentally, it should be noted that all the stages of fermentation but one occur within the muscles of a man running a hundred yards race (which a competent athlete will do without breathing—he only starts panting when he has finished). The one exception is that at the end of the chain of reactions the pyruvic acid, which in most yeasts is converted by way of acetaldehyde to alcohol, is in mammalian muscle transformed into lactic acid. The reactions are:

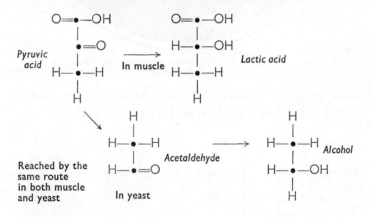

But, as is now well known, besides using this chain of reactions which is recognised as generally applicable to much of biological life, the particular mould strain *Penicillium notatum* also produces a small amount of the special substance called penicillin (Fig. 42). The outstanding pharmacological properties of penicillin are such that it has become the single

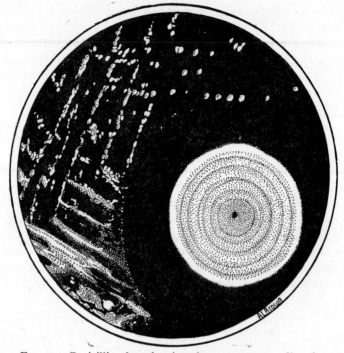

FIG. 42.　Penicillin plate showing clear zone surrounding the
mould colony

most important product of the pharmaceutical industry,
exceeding in value even aspirin. Its structure is this:

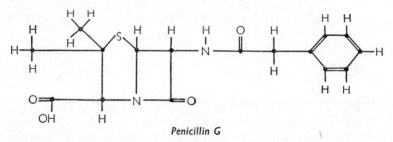

Penicillin **G**

Besides penicillin there are today twenty or so antibiotics
produced by different types of micro-organisms. These substances are used in the treatment of a wide diversity of medical

conditions, and several of them are also employed technically, for example as food preservatives in packaged chicken or added to the ice in trawlers to keep fish fresh until it is landed. All these substances are produced in substantial amounts in factories which use considerable skill in handling and extracting the material in marketable form but in which, nevertheless, the actual formation of the chemical substance is left to the often obscure and complex processes within a living organism.

One further example is, perhaps, of some interest. In 1928, a botanist in French Equatorial Africa discovered that a certain disease of cotton plants was due to a micro-organism called *Eremothecium ashbii*. Later, in 1935, it was observed that this organism contained within its living substance granules of a pure vitamin, now known as riboflavin. Today this micro-organism, just like the penicillin microbe, is grown in great vessels in large factories and the vitamin is extracted from it and sold by the pound. It is used to improve human diets, as a medicine for people suffering from vitamin deficiency, and on a very large scale in animal and poultry rations. Again, the factory process used to prepare it is quite complicated, as shown in Fig. 43. But its actual formation is performed by the living *Eremothecium*. Here is its structure:

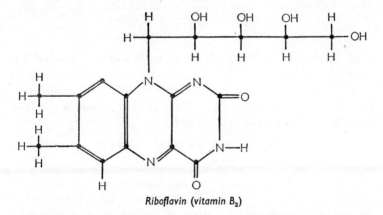

Riboflavin (vitamin B₂)

We have already discussed in this book the importance of catalysts in achieving so many of the practical results obtained from chemistry. Although we can claim to know something of how catalysts work, yet at the same time we need to confess that in many respects we are ignorant. Biological chemistry and the reactions that occur in it are extreme examples of inter-

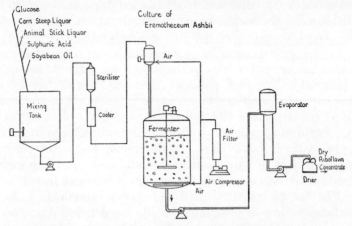

FIG. 43.   Culture of *Eremothecium ashbii* (riboflavin process)

locking, catalytically controlled chemical processes. We have seen, for example, that the "simple" Gay-Lussac equation for fermentation—

$$C_6H_{12}O_6 \longrightarrow 2CO_2 + 2C_2H_5OH$$
Glucose   Alcohol

is in real life (to use this phrase in its literal sense) a series of twelve interconnected and enzyme-activated chemical changes.

The apparently even simpler reaction arising, by implication, from Lavoisier's early studies of animal heat, namely the basic reaction for the use of glucose as fuel—

$$C_6H_{12}O_6 + 6O_2 \longrightarrow 6CO_2 + 6H_2O$$

is, in fact, even more complex.

The so-called "Krebs cycle" of reactions was the first to be elucidated, in 1950. The effect of the oxygen breathed in during respiration is brought to bear at the pyruvic acid stage of the fermentation process we have already described. What happens is shown in Fig. 44.

This complicated series of repeated changes takes place in the biochemistry of living tissues for two purposes. Firstly, at each of the three points in the cycle where CO_2 breaks off, energy is released. The second function of this intricate system is that, as shown in the diagram, it affords a spring-board for the formation of amino acids: aspartic acid, glutamic acid and alanine

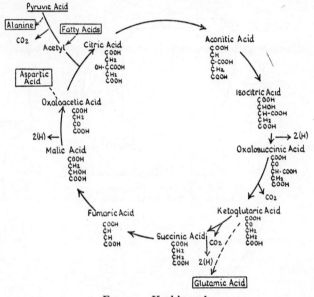

FIG. 44. Kreb's cycle

are marked. These are then available to be built into protein from which muscles and other tissues can be constructed.

But the complexity of biological chemistry which makes living people, animals and micro-organisms "go" has not even yet been fully described. In the 1950s, a series of further chemical substances was isolated—one by one—and their relationship to each other elucidated. The elaborate system that we, as higher animals, carry about with us and use, it seems, to release chemical energy from the glucose of our food, also exists in large part in green leaves, where many of the enzymes are caused to work in reverse: the light-energy of the sun, geared in through the chlorophyll molecule, reduces and converts into glucose the CO_2 from the air, which we now oxidise in these complicated ways in order to regain, in a controlled and gradual stream, the energy the sun originally put in. The energy-release system is called the "hexose-monophosphate cycle", and is shown in Fig. 45.

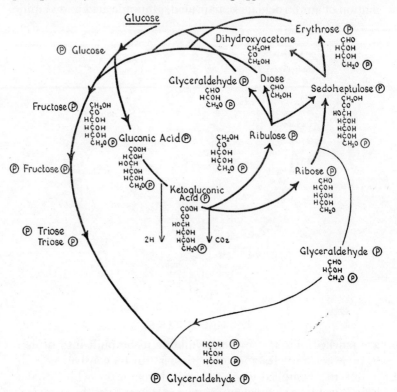

FIG. 45.   Hexose-monophosphate cycle

The way in which chlorophyll in the green leaves of plants "winds up" the system to produce glucose in the first place is not yet understood. The structure of chlorophyll is shown in Fig. 46.

What our present understanding of biochemistry is showing us is that the complex, catalytically operated systems by which fuel molecules, principally glucose, are oxidised and hence caused to release chemical energy, are interlocked with chemical mechanisms by which the chemical structures which compose living cells are built up. For example, the "Krebs cycle" while releasing energy also produces here and there a "matrix" upon which amino acids can be built up. Again, as we have just discussed, the "hexose-monophosphate cycle" is, it seems, not very different from the system by which plants use the energy

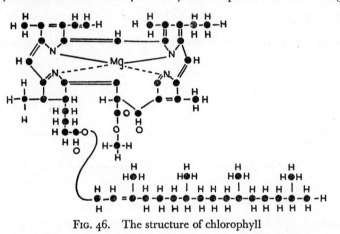

FIG. 46.   The structure of chlorophyll

of sunshine, harnessed through the green chlorophyll molecule, to build up glucose from carbon dioxide.

But amino acids and glucose, although not exactly simple compounds, are themselves only the building units of which the far more elaborate chemistry of living tissues is constructed. Furthermore, as is quite obvious, the stuff of which different animals are made—mammals, beetles, bacteria of diverse sorts, and so on—differs from species to species. How are these differences in chemical composition controlled?

The nucleus of almost all living cells contains a substance called deoxyribo-nucleic acid, D.N.A. for short. This compound has an immense molecule the structure of which is in the form of two corkscrews twined together. Evidence from experiments is gradually accruing that it is this D.N.A. that is the mould by which the whole growth of an animal is controlled. The D.N.A. molecule comprises at least a thousand twists in its corkscrew configuration and is made up of phosphate, a derivative of the special type of sugar called ribose and a pattern of half a dozen purine and pyrimidine "bases." These pieces of the D.N.A. molecule have the following structures:

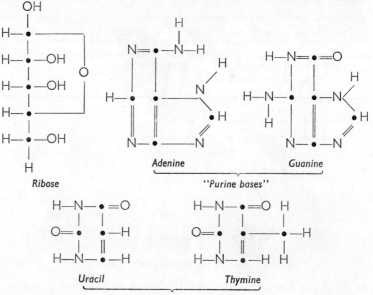

All these pieces are arranged and rearranged in a sequence of "code words" as it were all the way down the spiral of D.N.A. A diagram of D.N.A. is shown in Fig. 47.

D.N.A. is essential for most kinds of life, and is able to reproduce itself. A similar compound of approximately equal complexity, R.N.A., controls the increase in protein for growth. Loose amino acids fit on to the appropriate grooves and indentations of this molecule and when they peel off they are in the right proportion and the right order to compose the appropriate cellular tissue.

Basically, therefore, we can now see that the chemistry of living cells is concerned with two things. One is the release of energy. The other is the construction of complex tissues from simple chemical components.

The most obvious use of this latter function for practical human ends is in agriculture. Here we have the conversion of elementary nitrogen in, say, ammonium sulphate fertiliser, first into the protein of grass and then into beef—or wool. But

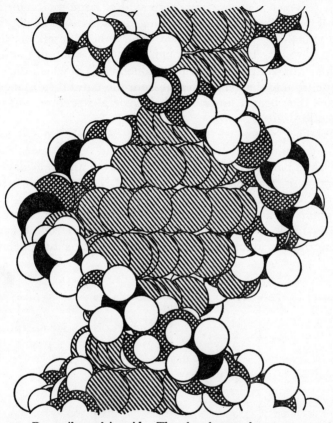

FIG. 47. Deoxyribonucleic acid. The phosphate and sugar are regularly linked in the very long chain in which the phosphate-sugar sequences are repeated over and over again.

as well as taking advantage of this biological chemistry as it exists in nature, that is, by using meat, and wool, and silk, and leather, we have also used our knowledge to imitate this chemistry ourselves. In Chapter 9 we shall be discussing "*polymers*", or at least those polymers that are of commercial

importance as "plastics." It is, therefore, important to realise
that protein, whether it appears as the casein in milk (from
which, if one wishes, buttons or umbrella handles can be made),
hair, silk, egg albumen or lean meat, is chemically a polymer.

A polymer is an organic compound of large molecular size
made up of one or more repeating units. Artificial "plastics"
are something like wood or leather or rubber or silk or whatever it may be because, although the composition of the individual unit compounds (called "monomers") of which they are
made up may be very different from the natural substance to
which they bear a similarity, their general structure is usually
broadly similar.

Proteins, which we are discussing now, are composed of
repeating units, which are the amino acids. As we have already
seen, the pattern of the design to which the amino acids must
conform is apparently fixed by the R.N.A. molecule which
serves, as it were, as a template.

There are a couple of dozen different amino acids. Some are
fairly simple in structure, some contain ring structures, and
some contain atoms of sulphur. Examples are shown below:

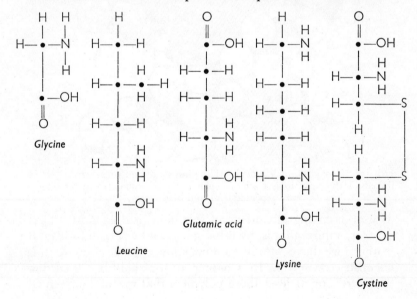

Glycine

Leucine

Glutamic acid

Lysine

Cystine

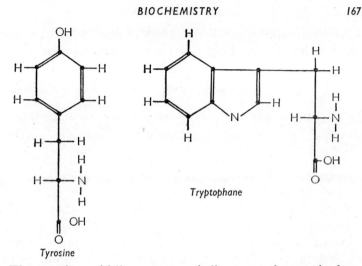

Tryptophane

Tyrosine

These amino acid "monomer units"—to use the terminology of manufactured plastics—link up with each other like this:

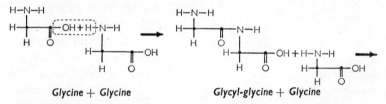

Glycine + Glycine   *Glycyl-glycine + Glycine*

and so on.

I have referred to such diverse materials as hair and wool and cheese (largely made up of the milk protein, casein) and leather and silk and lean meat all as examples of protein. But while the chemical nature of all these is similar inasmuch as they are all composed of linked patterns of amino acids, their physical structures are obviously different. These differing physical structures reflect the differences in the chemical configurations of their molecules.

The linkage —CO·NII—, that I have represented diagrammatically above by — • —N—H is a highly effective molecular

mechanism for the elaboration of substances of great diversity and complexity. The different types of amino acids, which offer some two dozen different kinds of links, some with extra possibilities of branching when a link has a second amino

group, $—\bullet—N$ (with H above and H below) or carboxyl group $—\bullet=O$ (with OH above), give even greater opportunities for the building up of different structures. Silk, for example, has a fully extended chain of linked amino groups thus:

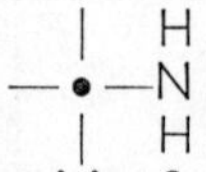

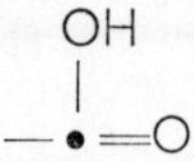

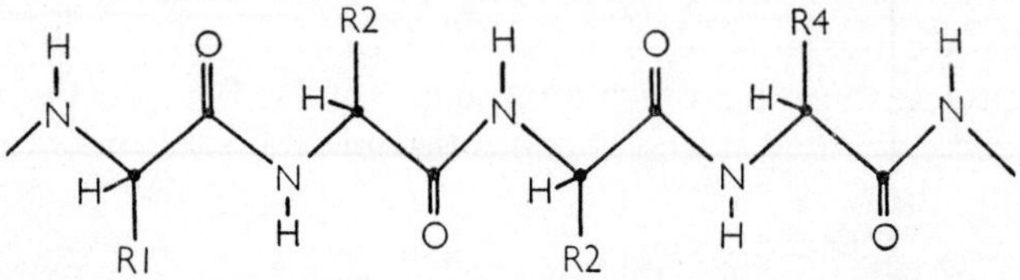

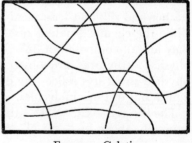

Wool, on the other hand, possesses a more "crinkled" molecular structure. Different again are such proteins as egg albumen and milk casein in which the chains are not stretched out in a fibre at all but, on the contrary, are all tangled and branched. Hence we get, on a larger bird's-eye view, a picture of the structure of keratin from silk like Fig. 48.

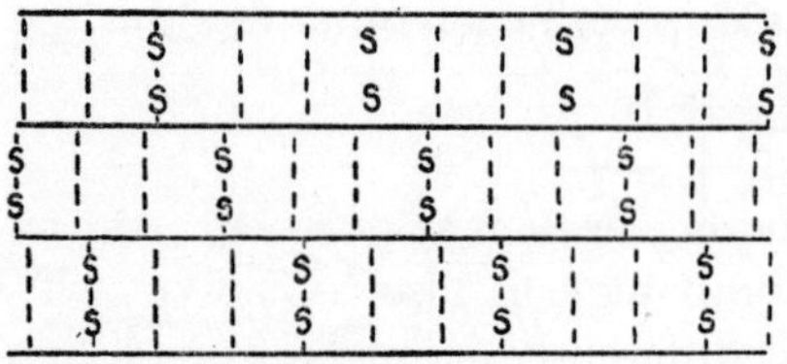

FIG. 48.   Keratin

That is to say, the amino acid chains are held together sideways by the "spare" linkages, some of which are sulphur links supplied by those amino acids that contain this element. Gelatin, on the other hand, which has quite different physical properties, is represented by Fig. 49.

It is, perhaps, worth noting that when it is desired to deform a protein structure, for example in the "permanent waving" of hair, one of the modern methods of going about it is first to treat

FIG. 49.   Gelatin

the structure with a solution of a "sulphydryl" compound, that is one supplying —SH groups, and then, when the desired bond has been accomplished mechanically, to fix the protein in its waved shape by neutralising the residual —SH's with an oxidising agent such as bromate. These chemicals are the basis of the "home perm."

As we have already seen in Chapter 6, another important group of "polymers" produced by the biochemistry of living cells are the starches and cellulose. These are built up out of sugars as the repeating "monomer" units. It is worth showing once again how starch is composed of chains of linked glucose units, thus:

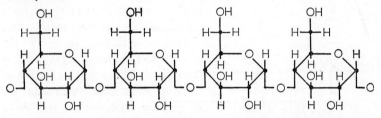

Cellulose, which is a major component of wood (and from which in turn paper is composed), is also a "polymer." Its chain stucture is somewhat differently arranged from starch—as one might infer from the practical observation that one can boil and eat potato but not paper.

A cellulose "chain" is chemically thus, as we showed before in Chapter 6.

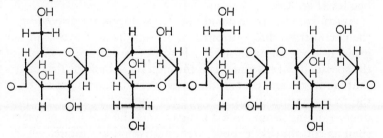

The significance of showing once again that the glucose "monomers" in cellulose chains are arranged in configuration first one way up and then the other way up whereas those in starch chains are all the same way round is this. Each stage by which the processes of biochemistry work is only made possible because of the existence of the appropriate catalyst (in biology these catalysts are chemically proteins of a very special nature called "enzymes"). Higher animals, including man, possess the appropriate enzymes for dealing with starch. These enzyme catalysts can break down starch chains by digestion to allow the energy-release enzymes to use the resulting glucose units as fuel. On the other hand, glucose units derived from elsewhere can be built up into starch—animal starch is specially named "glycogen"—for storage as an emergency fuel supply in the liver or muscles.

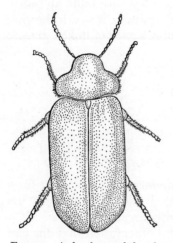

Higher animals, however, do not possess the appropriate "zip-fastener slide" enzymes capable of dealing with cellulose made up of glucose units joined by "beta linkage". Plants possess enzymes for building up the polymeric structure of wood, but the biological families able to break down cellulose are restricted to such creatures as the micobes in the

FIG. 50.   A death-watch beetle

digestive machinery of ruminants, white ants or death-watch beetles (Fig. 50).

Apart from the pure delight of the triumphant unravelling of the chemistry of life, one of the most significant features in our growing understanding of biochemistry is our appreciation of the specificity of enzymes. It is through these biological catalysts that life works and that all the variety of substances produced in the fermentation industries, the diversity of agricultural products ranging from milk to sugar and the natural polymers such as cotton, silk, rubber, wool and wood are made.

9

Plastics

The first achievement of the science of chemistry was the winning of metals. The easiest metals came first. Gold, the extraction of which requires hardly any chemistry at all because it is metallic gold in its natural state, was used very early. In the Bronze Age man acquired some rude practical knowledge of oxidation and reduction which enabled him to recover the copper and zinc and tin and lead mixture from its ore by reduction. Later came the less easily handled iron, and the chemical understanding which allows us to reduce such modern materials as aluminium and magnesium has only come in the most recent past.

Overlapping its basic contribution of metals with their multifarious uses as tools and machines, chemistry in its second phase has contributed an ever-extending list of "chemicals"—drugs, gunpowder, artificial fertilisers, dyes, antibiotics.

There is a third great phase of applied chemistry, which is as important as either of the other two, and unlike them it has come with a rush and is almost completely an achievement of our present modern age. The different woods—oak, mahogany, box-wood, deal, walnut or maple—from which furniture, boats, bats and articles of all sorts have been made; ivory, horn, bone; shoe leather, kid, doe-skin, crocodile skin, pig-skin, wash-leather; wool, cotton, silk, linen—all these materials have been used for ages as nature provided them. And because it has only been properly understood for the last century or so that the products of living things possess a molecular structure which can be chemically interpreted in the same way as Epsom salts or sulphuric acid, these diverse useful materials are even now hardly considered to be "chemicals." Today, however, for the first time it has been shown to be possible by the application of scientific knowledge to make by chemistry "artificial" woods, and leathers and ivories and rubbers, and textiles and, even beyond these, to invent new substances like cellophane and perspex and nylon that are improvements on anything known to nature.

The beginning of this great new advance in applied organic chemistry took place almost exactly a hundred years ago. But the first polymer "plastic" was not a new chemical construction in the full sense. It involved rather the new use of one of the principal polymers already existing in nature, namely, cellulose, which is the main structural material in wood and other vegetable materials, for instance cotton.

In the 1860s the demand for ivory was so great that vast herds of elephants were being slaughtered in an attempt to supply the market. In 1863, therefore, an American manufacturer of billiard balls offered a reward of ten thousand dollars to anyone who could invent an ivory substitute. The two prophets of the new chemical age who won the prize were Isaiah and John Hyatt.

Thirty years before, Professor Braconnot in France had discovered that sawdust or cotton treated with nitric acid produced a viscous substance which could be dissolved in vinegar and deposited as films or made into shaped articles. Later, a chemist called Schönbein treated cotton with a mixture of nitric and sulphuric acids and found that the resulting *nitrocellulose* could be dissolved in ether or alcohol. The exact way in which the operation was done was soon found to be very important. Under some circumstances the resultant "gun cotton" was highly explosive and many accidents occurred in its early manufacture. Furthermore, the behaviour of the nitrocellulose depended to a large degree on the solvent in which it was dissolved. One of the ingredients used in making the "celluloid" billiard balls was camphor. Amyl acetate was discovered in 1882 as a good solvent for nitrocellulose, and later ethyl acetate.

It is now clear that cellulose can be nitrated to three differing degrees, like this:

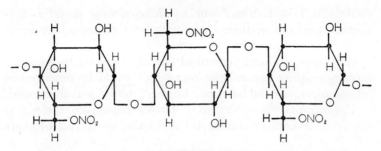

1. Polymer of units $C_6H_7O_2(OH)_2ONO_2$ (6·8 per cent. of nitrogen).

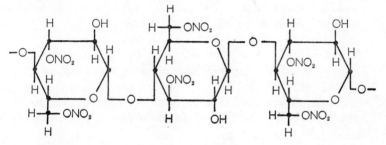

2. Polymer of units $C_6H_7O_2(OH)(ONO_2)_2$ (11·3 per cent. of nitrogen).

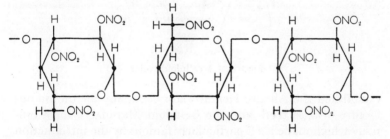

3. Polymer of units $C_6H_7O_2(ONO_2)_3$ (14·2 per cent. of nitrogen).

After sufficient practical experience with nitrocellulose had been obtained, some of it painful and disastrous and involving explosions, it was finally discovered that mixtures containing 12·2–13·8 per cent. of nitrogen were explosive; that mixtures containing 11·5–12·2 per cent. of nitrogen were useful as lacquers; and that mixtures containing least nitrogen, say 10·5–11·5 per cent., could be used as plastics.

Here then, by using chemical means primarily to make an already existing natural polymer which could be dissolved in an organic liquid and handled, the first "plastic" was developed.

The original inventors went far to popularise their new material. Besides producing billiard balls, the Hyatt brothers

FIG. 51.   A celluloid collar

established the Albany Dental Plate Company for the manufacture of false teeth and the Celluloid Manufacturing Company which made itself particularly famous by the introduction of celluloid collars (Fig. 71).

Nowadays, celluloid and "xylonite," as it is also called, and other cellulose plastics such as *ethyl-cellulose* and *cellulose acetate*, which while similar to nitrocellulose are not so readily inflammable, are used for an immense range of things. The material itself is dissolved in an organic solvent and is then mixed with a selected "plasticiser." One of the earliest and best was, as I have said, camphor. But we can hardly claim that the choice was based on logical chemical principles—plasticisers are usually hit upon by luck or intuition or experience on the basis of whether they "work" or not. The mixture is stirred and then rolled out into sheets or extruded into rods or chopped up into flakes. From these are made "tortoiseshell" spectacle frames, cinema film, the barrels of fountain-pens, "cellophane" wrapping film or sausage casing, piano keys, combs, brush handles and many other articles.

The cellulose compounds we have been talking about are called "thermoplastics" because they soften when they are heated. Under appropriate conditions they can be made to assume a syrupy consistency and can then be drawn out into fine threads. "Artificial silk", invented by Chardonnet in 1889, was simply nitro-cellulose. Although it made an elegant silky textile it was, of course, highly inflammable. Rayon, invented by Cross and Bevan in England in 1893, is made of cellulose itself, brought into solution by treatment with a hot alkali (sodium hydroxide) and then extruded through very fine holes.

The chemical modification of a natural substance such as cellulose is not the only example of the adaptation by chemists of an existing polymer as an industrial plastic. Early in the century, there was a quite widely used German patent for using casein, the protein from milk, as a plastic. It will be remembered that proteins are polymers built up out of amino acids. By "condensing" the casein with formaldehyde a tough, readily fabricated mass of "Galalith" was produced. More recently the protein from groundnuts has been used to produce a textile fibre not very unlike wool. This material is called "Ardil".

The first really artificial plastic to achieve any degree of eminence was *bakelite*, invented by a Belgian, L. H. Baekeland, in 1909. This depends upon the chemical reaction between phenol and formaldehyde. The exact chemical mechanism of this reaction is obscure. For instance, it appears to occur in stages and the later parts of the chemical operation are made to proceed only when the simpler "moulding powder" arising from the first stages is squeezed under a pressure of 2,000 lb. per sq. in. or so. The first part of the reaction seems to be as follows:

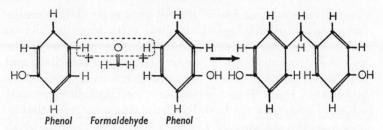

Phenol　　Formaldehyde　　Phenol

⚑ The first phenol-formaldehyde compounds continue to combine with additional formaldehyde and phenol molecules until a three-dimensional polymer is built up. And this is a block of bakelite. Its structure in diagrammatic form can be written:

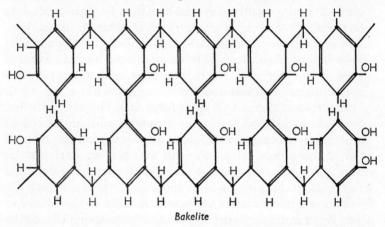

Bakelite

Since its original discovery just fifty years ago bakelite has become a substance of great commercial importance. It is used very widely in making electrical equipment, for knobs and gadgets of all sorts, for wireless sets and, indeed, in all manner of things where a light, hard, strong and resistant material is required, and is often formed into intricate shapes. As we have already mentioned, bakelite (and related plastics) today use enormous amounts of phenol made from coal; nevertheless, its structure demonstrates, like many examples of applied chemistry, a considerable mixture of logical scientific thinking and, as with inspired cooking, an element of empiricism.

For example, when Baekeland took up his work in 1905,

Bayer in Germany and Morgan in Britain had already recorded that a resinous mass was produced when formaldehyde was reacted with phenol. But this was not "chemistry" to the ideas of the time. Baekeland, however, pursued the matter further and found that the results he got—as in so much else in real as distinct from textbook chemistry—were dependent on a catalyst (and, on the face of it, particular catalysts rarely seem to possess obvious chemical justification). He found that when he used acid as his catalyst he got a permanently fusible product. On the other hand, alkali would catalyse a favourable reaction but if too much was used the reaction became uncontrollable. By using smaller amounts of alkali he was able to guide the progress of events. In his patents he described three forms of bakelite, A, B and C. The first was liquid while hot and was soluble in organic solvents; the B-form was viscous and partly soluble; while the C-form, after being moulded hot in a "bakeliser" (a chamber in which pressure could be applied), was infusible and insoluble.

The notion that a comparatively small chemical unit such as phenol could be combined over and over again to produce a plastic soon became accepted as a general principle. Bakelite, particularly when mixed up with a "filler" of some sort, say sawdust, was a valuable general-purpose material—but it was brown. Searching round for a monomer other than phenol to link together with formaldehyde, chemists soon came upon urea as a cheap, suitable compound. Furthermore, like phenol, it has two available linkages which allow the gradual building up of a large polymer structure, shown on next page.

This urea-formaldehyde plastic can be made quite colourless, indeed almost transparent like glass. It is widely used for cups and tumblers under the name of "Beetle" ware.

I have said that at the time when Baekeland was experimenting with the phenol-formaldehyde reaction fifty years ago, the production of the sticky masses he was studying was not considered by orthodox students to be "real" chemistry. However, when the great industrial possibilities of bakelite became apparent, chemists began to review with intense energy the various types of "condensation" reactions that were then

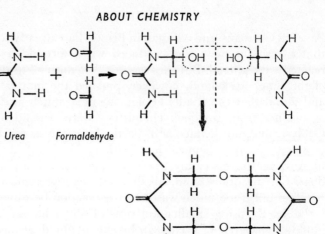

Urea   Formaldehyde

known. In America, particularly, Carothers of the Du Pont Company undertook a fundamental research into the synthesis and structure of large molecules which lasted for ten years from the 1920s to the 1930s.

It is salutary to note that *styrene* was first produced in 1866 and its polymerisation observed in 1909. That is about fifty years ago. Today, more than 120,000 tons a year are used for the manufacture of all sorts of things from battery boxes to synthetic rubber. The chemical reaction in summary is:

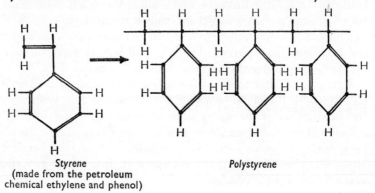

Styrene   Polystyrene
(made from the petroleum
chemical ethylene and phenol)

Even more striking (and perhaps humiliating) is the fact that the polymerisation of *vinyl chloride* was first recorded more than a century ago, in 1835. The chemical reaction in summary is:

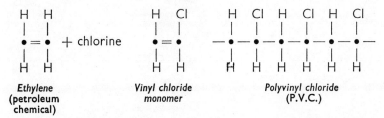

| Ethylene (petroleum chemical) | Vinyl chloride monomer | Polyvinyl chloride (P.V.C.) |

Vinyl chloride itself is a gas at room temperature, and a good deal of "know-how" had to be acquired before a commercial product could be made out of the polymer. Today, however, it is a popular and widely used material. It is best known to the ordinary person in the form of plastic sheeting from which the modern light and attractive coloured or transparent rain-coats are made (Fig. 52).

Another important "modern" group of plastics is based on *methyl acrylate* which was first polymerised in 1880. Again the starting material was ethylene, usually from petroleum. By chemical manipulation, a methyl group — •—H is attached to the methyl methacrylate monomer which is then polymerised, thus:

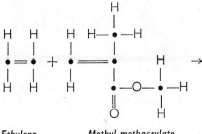

Ethylene   Methyl methacrylate

FIG. 52.   A P.V.C. mackintosh

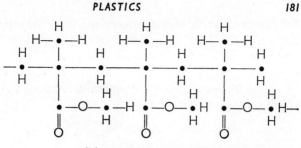

Polymethyl methacrylate ("Perspex")

The chain of polymethyl methacrylate, that is "Perspex," is long and branched, and its physical properties are such that the roofs of "bubble cars" or the tops of aircraft cockpits can be made from it.

One of the apparently simplest plastics from the chemical point of view is *polythene*. In chemical structure it is *poly-*

Fig. 53.   Polythene objects

ethylene. It is widely used in the manufacture of electrical equipment, and is known in the home in the form of washing-up bowls, squeeze-bottles, and polythene bags for keeping things in and, more recently, in the form of water pipes (Fig. 53).

Polythene was a British discovery made by Imperial Chemical Industries in 1938. It was then found that ethylene gas could be caused to polymerise into long chains of a thousand or more carbon atoms if it were compressed under enormous pressures of 30,000 lb. per sq. in. at a temperature of 200° C. The chemistry of its manufacture is this:

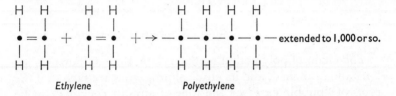

Ethylene   Polyethylene

that is, far beyond naturally occurring paraffin chains. These chains are also branched here and there.

Obviously, the construction of a polythene plant which could safely withstand the tremendous pressures required was a difficult and expensive matter which during the last twenty years has involved I.C.I. in considerable capital outlay. What, then, must have been the feelings of the directors when within months it became known that Professor Karl Ziegler of the Max Plank Institute for Coal Research in Essen had developed —need I say—a catalyst capable of bringing about the polymerisation of ethylene at normal atmospheric pressure! This Ziegler catalyst is made out of aluminium and titanium.

The new, "low-pressure" polyethylene has a long unbranched chain and is in many respects an improvement on the polythene we know. It is stronger, smoother and will resist higher temperatures. This means that it can be sterilised. But to the philosophical mind its sudden appearance again underlines the existence, side by side with our growing understanding of chemistry, of the more halting growth of a glimmering awakening to the parallel mechanism of catalysis.

Cellulose, of which paper and much of wood is composed, is a natural polymer made up of repeating units of sugar, —$C_6H_{10}O_5$—. Perspex, as we have seen, is in its way, an artificial "wood," made up of repeating units of —C_5H_8O—. Polythene, even more simply, is a repeating compound of

—CH₂— units. These artificial polymers and the carbohydrate polymers, cellulose, starch and the like, make up one great natural polymer group. Cotton belongs to this category. But there is another even more important natural polymer group, namely, the proteins, which compose such materials as muscle, leather, wool, hair and silk. Proteins, we have said before, are made up of repeating units containing nitrogen as well as carbon, hydrogen and oxygen. Although the achievement of Carothers in spotting in 1939 and 1940 that artificial polymers with particularly attractive properties could be made by condensing nitrogen-containing compounds with carbon-hydrogen-and-oxygen compounds was very remarkable, it is not so surprising to us with our hindsight that it could be done. After all, were there not the natural polymers wool and hair?

The most famous of artificial "polyamide" polymers is *nylon*. It is made by condensing a series of hexamethylene-diamine units alternately with adipic acid, thus:

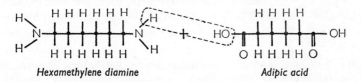

Hexamethylene diamine   Adipic acid

The reaction is brought about by heating the two components together at 280° C. in an inert atmosphere of nitrogen. The melted nylon thus formed is then pumped through fine holes into cold water and the resulting fibre wound on to reels (Fig. 54). It is a romantic thought that this material, so popular today, is made from the raw materials of coal, which gives phenol to form the adipic acid, and air, which provides the nitrogen which, first "fixed" as we have earlier described to give ammonia, is later combined with a carbon skeleton from the coal to produce hexamethylene diamine.

The invention of nylon was not only important in itself; it led in the first place to a number of parallel "polyamide" plastics of similar type. An interesting example is a softer type of nylon-like fibre called "perlon", which uses cyclohexanone instead of the adipic acid employed in nylon. A curious fact is that perlon, now quite widely manufactured in Germany, is one of the few combinations of this type not covered by the original Du Pont patents protecting the production of nylon itself.

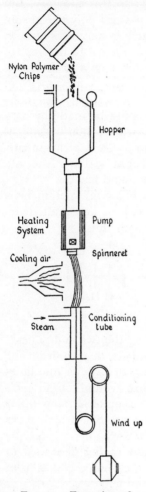

But the second and more important aspect of the invention of nylon was the realisation that polymers might be consciously designed to possess certain desired characteristics. Nylon has quite a long chain-structure and after the molecule has been formed the fibre is stretched. This stretching has been shown by X-ray examination to align the molecules in parallel. That is, it "combs out," as it were, the molecular tangle and thus produces the strong fibre that we recognise as characteristic. It is now realised that the longer the molecular chains are, the tougher is the material. Furthermore, by "co-polymerising" one polymer with one type of characteristics with another group of monomers giving different characteristics, we can obtain a product with intermediate properties.

In practice, this aspect of polymer chemistry quickly becomes very complex. Polymer chemists use a variety of techniques to measure the completeness of polymerisation, the length of the chains obtained, and the degree to which co-polymers like vinyl acetate, vinyl chloride, butadiene (the rubber-forming monomer) and so on have become integrated with the ultimate substance produced.

Fig. 54.   Extrusion of nylon

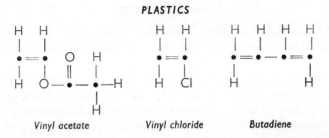

Vinyl acetate *Vinyl chloride* *Butadiene*

Terylene, discovered in the 1940s about ten years after nylon, is often quoted as a polymer which was planned to possess the properties it does. Two English chemists, Whinfield and Dickson, invented a synthetic plastic which could be drawn into fibres. The monomer units they used were—at least to some degree—consciously selected as being likely to produce something with properties rather like those of wool. The two monomers used were terephthalic acid and ethylene glycol. Their structures are as follows:

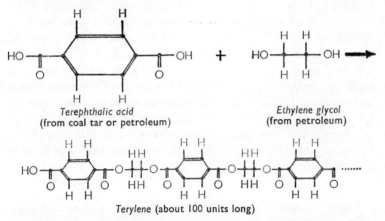

Terephthalic acid Ethylene glycol
(from coal tar or petroleum) (from petroleum)

Terylene (about 100 units long)

We have reviewed a number of the organic substances that can be caused to take part in polymerisation reactions. Chemists have now become familiar with such reactions as those between phenol and formaldehyde which gives bakelite, between urea and formaldehyde (giving "Beetle" ware); between one styrene molecule and another, giving the sort of material of which refrigerators are constructed; and between one ethylene molecule and another to yield polythene.

Although the invention of plastics came upon the scientific scene almost one would imagine, as a surprise, the amount of information now available is sufficient to form a more or less coherent scientific system. The literature of plastics chemistry is today very voluminous. There are a number of important text-books and several learned scientific journals are published on the subject. The relationship between the chemistry of the very large polymer molecules and the physical structure of the resultant plastic, whether it be a drawn-out fibre like nylon or terylene or a solid block like bakelite or perspex, is also becoming understood. Nevertheless, this whole remarkable development of chemical knowledge is haunted by ignorance. This, perhaps, is not surprising when we recall again that Baekeland only invented bakelite in 1909, fifty or so years ago, and Carothers, who more than any other man was responsible for the jump forward in this subject of "chemical building," carried out his researches a mere twenty-five years ago.

The most striking example of the surprises that ignorance can spring on our self-confident march forward in the chemical technology of plastics is that of polythene. I have already referred to the development of "low pressure" methods of making polythene using "Ziegler catalysts," which, if they have not rendered high-pressure manufacturing techniques obsolete, have at least made their review urgently necessary. But the whole business goes back even further than this out of the realm of understood scientific principle and into the area of inspired chance.

Vinyl compounds, notably vinyl chloride $\underset{\underset{H}{|}}{\overset{\overset{H}{|}}{\bullet}} = \underset{\underset{H}{|}}{\overset{\overset{Cl}{|}}{\bullet}}$ had been known to polymerise over since 1835, as we have already said.

One might have imagined, therefore, that ethylene $\underset{\underset{H}{|}}{\overset{\overset{H}{|}}{\bullet}} = \underset{\underset{H}{|}}{\overset{\overset{H}{|}}{\bullet}}$ would have been expected to polymerise as well. In fact, no one took any particular interest in this possibility. Nevertheless, when in the course of a systematic research programme chemists in the I.C.I. Alkali Division who were studying the reactions of ethylene and benzaldehyde under high pressure observed a waxy product coating the walls of the reaction vessel, they had the insight to recognise it as a polymer of ethylene. But when they tried to polymerise ethylene they did not succeed until they used a high-pressure apparatus with a leak in it! It was when the experimenters pumped in more ethylene to keep up the pressure in their leaky vessel that they eventually found that in order to succeed a small amount of oxygen had to be present as well. The oxygen takes no direct part in the chemical reaction. It seems to be needed, however, even in the process of making polythene the hard way under enormous pressure, as a catalyst. Here again then we have the accidental discovery of a fact which does not fit into any kind of systematic theory being the key needed to achieve a chemical operation.

It is perhaps interesting at this point to stop and consider—not what we do *not* know—but, on the contrary, the very remarkable burgeoning that has taken place all at once in the last twenty years or so of the newer chemical industry based on the process of polymerisation that we have been talking about.

Right up to the 1930s, the expression "chemical industry" brought to mind thoughts of metallurgy, that is the recovery of metals from their ores by the chemical process of reduction, or the separation of one metal from another, or the combination of several together. Then there was the "fixation" of nitrogen from the air to produce ammonia or nitrates for fertilisers; or the manufacture of sulphuric acid. In the field of organic chemistry, the chemical industry of fifty years ago implied the production of coal gas, the separation of benzene and the multitude of other organic molecules in coal tar for the manufacture of dyes, drugs or complex organic substances with half a hundred uses. But today a revolution has occurred. It is, perhaps, best illustrated by citing the enormous industrial enterprise being pushed forward by Imperial Chemical

Industries on the borders of Durham and Yorkshire in northern England.

On the Durham side of the river Tees is Billingham. Here is an advanced example of what might be called "traditional" chemical industry, centred round a plant for the "fixation" of nitrogen for the manufacture of fertilisers, explosives, ammonia and nitric acid. There is also a great works for the hydrogenation of coal for automobile fuels as described in Chapter 7. On the Yorkshire side of the river at Wilton is an area of two thousand acres on which one hundred million pounds sterling is being spent. Here, either already in existence or being built, are eighteen separate factories. Of these, eleven are solely occupied in producing polymers and two more devote a large proportion of their output to the same purpose. That is to say, whereas up to now chemical industry has been occupied in *doing* something—oxidising, reducing, producing energy, colouring with a dyestuff, exerting drug or vitamin effects, splitting with acid or alkali—this new-type chemical enterprise is putting carbon atoms together to *make* new kinds of matter: bakelite, synthetic rubbers, perspex, polythene, terylene— materials simulating such natural substances as wood, ivory, wool, cotton or hair. Chemists, that is to say, have learned the trick of making stuff similar in its general chemical composition to these natural polymers.

In chemistry, nothing is made out of nothing. Or to put it differently, the substances chemists make—and, for that matter, the substances made by the biochemical processes of nature—can only be produced from such raw materials as are available. All the natural substances, the cellulose of wood and cotton or the casein buttons made from the protein of milk, are made principally from carbon derived from the carbon dioxide gas of the air "fixed" by the chemistry of photosynthesis in green leaves. The artificial polymers made in chemical factories, on the other hand, are made from "banked" carbon derived from stores of coal or of petroleum.

At the Billingham-Wilton "conurbation" of factories both coal and oil are used as the basic sources of carbon. A crude-oil "cut" is "cracked" in one factory unit to supply ethylene

which is polymerised into polythene in another unit. More
ethylene is converted in another unit into ethylene oxide with
the use of chlorine made from brine at a third unit. And the
ethylene oxide itself is converted to ethylene glycol in a fourth
unit for polymerisation in due course in a fifth factory devoted
to the manufacture of terylene fibre, with para-xylene made in
a sixth factory!

At other factories, benzene derived from coal is used to make
nylon; phenol also from coal is polymerised with formaldehyde

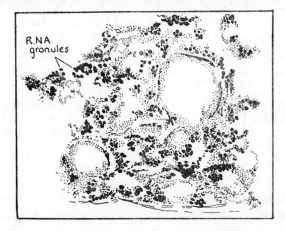

FIG. 55.   Electron micrograph of section through first body of motor neuron
of colliculus facialis of rat (after Palade)

to make a bakelite-type plastic; while formaldehyde in another
unit is polymerised with urea to make a different type of
plastic.

It is not altogether easy to foresee where this modern power
to construct very large organic molecules is going to lead. In
the past, our feet used to wear out our socks. Today, some of
the new "invented" textile fibres are so tough that socks made
from them have an abrasive effect on the skin and the fibres
must be mixed with a proportion of an "old fashioned" fibre
such as wool to prevent the socks from wearing away the feet.

The present chemical age is to a major degree the age of
large molecules. In the field of biochemistry we have reached

an understanding of the chemical structure of the enormous *nucleic acid* molecules. These are so big that, though they cannot be seen through a normal optical microscope, they can be "seen" with an electron microscope (Fig. 55). This, though an elaborate instrument, is in principle merely a device for focusing electron beams by suitably arranged magnetic fields, instead of light beams with appropriately selected lenses. And in the same way, the polymer chemists, like the biochemists, can "see" the molecular structure of the very large molecules they make artificially.

Artificial rubber can be made by polymerising butadiene and styrene, thus:

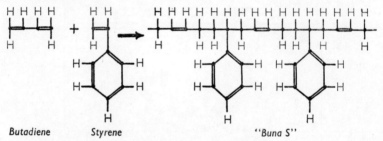

Butadiene   Styrene   "Buna S"

Its soft springy consistency is due, it now appears, to the fact that the chemical configuration of its molecule is a random

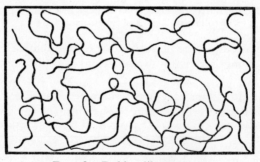

FIG. 56.　Rubber-like structure

collection of tangled and twisted chains of different lengths, fixed together here and there by "co-valent" chemical bonds (Fig. 56).

In the phenol-formaldehyde plastics of which bakelite is the best-known example, the several chains are long and tangled, and are also so firmly fixed together by chemical bonds as strong as the different links of the chains themselves that the

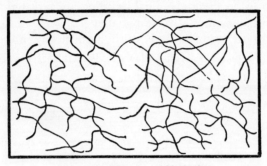

FIG. 57. Structure of bakelite

whole block can almost be thought of as one single molecule. This explains the hard stiffness of the plastic. Its structure is shown in Fig. 57.

Nylon, which, as will be remembered, is produced by polymerising 6-carbon-chain (and 2-nitrogen) units of hexamethylene diamine with 6-carbon-chain adipic acid units, forms a smoother chain polymer than many other plastics, thus:

And even after polymerisation is complete and the molecular chains are made, the nylon fibres are mechanically stretched. This, in fact, achieves a molecular "combing" effect so that the structure of the final substance has the form shown in Fig. 58.

Today our advanced chemical knowledge gives us command over the construction of a wide range of solid materials with properties excelling those of natural substances. We understand a good deal about their chemical composition and about their atomic architecture. There well may be surprises in store as one new catalyst after another is discovered—partly by taking thought and partly by luck. And these catalysts may well enable us to do more chemical building and arranging and to make more and more diverse polymers.

Up till now stored carbon, in the past mostly in the form of coal, has been used as a source of energy—both heat energy

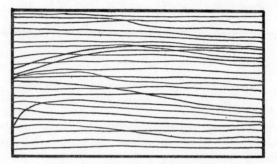

FIG. 58.   Structure of nylon fibre

and chemical energy to reduce metals from their ores. The forests of England, the Great Weald itself, were destroyed to smelt the early iron for industry. We still use some of our dwindling coal supplies for the same purpose. But some of the rest of the coal, and some of the carbon in oil as well, which is now being recklessly oxidised in our motor cars, can clearly be better employed as a source material for plastics to take the place of the vanished wood and of metal also. After all, chemistry has a good deal to say about the substitute energy we now have available from radioactive elements. This is the final topic for the brief review of chemical knowledge that I am trying to encompass in this book.

10

Atomic Energy and the Ultimate Constitution of Chemical Substance

In all ordinary chemical processes atoms are quite stable and behave as if they were indivisible particles. Indeed, the basic definition of an "atom" of any particular element is that it is the ultimate particle of an elemental substance that is different from all other substances. The chemical character of an atom of any element depends, as we saw in Chapter 2, on the number of electrons in its outermost "shell." These, the so-called valency electrons, link it together or hold it apart from other atoms in the formation of compound molecules, or in breaking them down. The combination, recombination and decomposition of molecules is usually accompanied by an exchange of energy. As we have now seen, with one single group of exceptions, all the energy in the world is derived from chemical reactions: the burning of coal or petroleum and the biochemical breakdown of food in living creatures are alike examples of the oxidation of reduced carbon compounds. There are other examples of chemical energy too, some of which we have discussed. But one great group of energy sources are exceptions to this statement: the warmth of the sun with all its attributes of falling rain and blowing wind and the very revolution of the earth itself and its moon are due, not to chemical energy, but to atomic energy.

Ever since 1896 it has been recognised that although the atoms of most chemical elements are stable, a few of those with very high atomic weights, such as uranium with an atomic weight of 238, and radium with an atomic weight of 226, exhibit spontaneous atomic degeneration. They gradually decay and as they do so they turn themselves into elements of something else, at the same time emitting energy in the form of radioactivity.

It is now known that the radioactivity of radium is due to the continuous loss of "alpha particles." These alpha particles are, in fact, the nucleus of a helium atom.

In Chapter 2, I set out the structure of helium diagrammatically as in Fig. 59. The two orbital electrons possess negative electrical charges. Consequently, in order that the atom may hold together as a stable unit, its nucleus must possess two positive electrical charges. In fact, the nucleus of an atom of

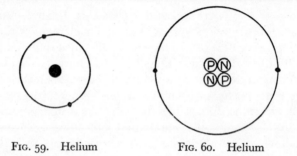

FIG. 59.   Helium   FIG. 60.   Helium

helium is made up of four comparatively heavy units, two protons, possessing positive charges, and two neutrons, possessing no charges at all. Diagrammatically, the whole thing could be drawn as in Fig. 60.

If this is the structure, as at present understood, of the nucleus of helium, the second simplest element there is, with an atomic weight of 4, the complexity of the nucleus of a heavy element like radium, with an atomic weight of 226, can be readily appreciated. The stresses and strains within such a nucleus packed with neutrons and with positively charged protons, lead, as I have just said, to the emission at high speed of alpha particles, each a helium nucleus, and each weighing about 8000 times as much as an electron. In 1911, Ernest Rutherford used a narrow stream of the alpha particles from radium as a probe to show that the apparently solid chemical structure of a thin metal plate was in fact made up of a web of widely scattered heavy particles (the atomic nuclei of the metal atoms, capable, if struck, of deflecting an alpha particle) and wide open spaces in which electrons circled in the different orbits of each atomic shell. The alpha particles passed straight through the open spaces, being only slightly slowed up by their impact with the comparatively light electrons.

Another important discovery, by which the physicists continued their elucidation of the nature of chemical elements, took place in 1919. This was the year in which Rutherford found that if he bombarded nitrogen sufficiently vigorously with alpha particles he could get one of them right into the nitrogen

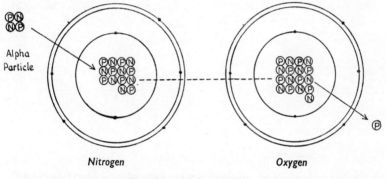

Nitrogen   Oxygen

FIG. 61.   Alpha particles

nucleus. The tension set up by this accretion of a particle containing two positive charges caused a partial disruption of the nitrogen nucleus. In fact, a hydrogen nucleus, that is a proton, was shot out. But the nitrogen nucleus, now being one proton to the good, was transmuted into an oxygen nucleus (Fig. 61).

Strictly speaking, this reaction does not deserve a place in a book about chemistry. Chemical operations have up to the present era been concerned with the interrelations between the "orbital" electrons by which atoms combine to form the mixed molecules we recognise in the world around us. The energy released when, for example, the carbon, nitrogen and hydrogen atoms in trinitro-toluene (T.N.T.) combine with oxygen is substantial. Conversely, the energy that needs to be put into iron ore in smelting (that is, to dissociate the oxygen

from the ore) or to polymerise ethylene to get polythene is considerable. But for neither kind of chemical reaction is the
amount of energy of anything like the same order of magnitude
as that required to cause a change in the nucleus of a nitrogen
atom. These types of reactions and these very large magnitudes
of energy are customarily considered to belong to physics
rather than to chemistry.

When we identify a substance as an element we imply that it
is a material that cannot be simplified or split up by ordinary
chemical means and which is different from all other elements.
In 1913 F. Soddy made the remarkable observation that it
was possible to obtain two substances with identical chemical

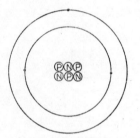   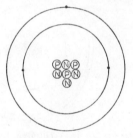

Fɪɢ. 62 Lithium (Lɪ⁶)   Fɪɢ. 63 Lithium (Lɪ⁷)

properties yet one of which had a different atomic weight from
the other. It was only after Chadwick had discovered the
existence of neutrons in 1932 that the full explanation of this
phenomenon became apparent.

The element lithium possesses three electrons circling round
its nucleus. Each of these of course, has a negative electrical
charge. They are counterbalanced by the presence in the
nucleus of the lithium atom of three protons, each with a
positive electrical charge. As well as these, there are three
neutrons, giving an atomic weight of about 6 (Fig. 62).

But in addition to Li^6, there is another isotope of lithium
known as Li^7. This possesses the same number of protons and
electrons, that is three, but instead of three neutrons its nucleus
contains four. This brings its atomic weight to 7 (Fig. 63). In

actual fact, the lithium normally encountered is a mixture of these two isotopes and has an atomic weight of 6·940. An *isotope*, therefore, is a substance the nucleus of whose atom differs from that of its "parent" by possessing a different number of neutrons.

It is now known that out of the first 83 elements ranging in the periodic table from hydrogen up to bismuth, 59 possess natural, stable isotopes. A number of them, indeed, possess several isotopes. For example, there are five natural isotopes of zinc, six isotopes of calcium, and seven isotopes of barium. The two natural isotopes of hydrogen have achieved some fame. The commoner hydrogen atom is made up of one proton and one

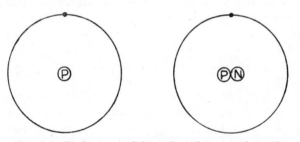

Fig. 64.   Hydrogen and deuterium (heavy hydrogen)

electron. The isotope has a proton and a neutron in its nucleus and is often called deuterium or "heavy hydrogen." Molecules of common water are written H_2O, whereas "heavy water" made up from the deuterium isotope is written D_2O (Fig. 64).

Naturally radioactive elements, such as radium and thorium and uranium, as I have said, emit *alpha particles*. These are the nuclei of helium atoms moving at a great pace. They are heavy, positively charged and are stopped by a few centimetres of air. There are also *beta rays*, which are electrons, negatively charged, light but very fast-moving and travelling rather farther through air. And finally there are *gamma rays*, which are not particles at all but short-wave radiation like X-rays, and with even greater powers of penetrating matter. These rays do not come off as a steady stream, but as each atom explodes it gives off its appropriate ray or particle. Naturally radioactive elements are all very heavy with, in consequence, large, complex and consequently unstable nuclei.

In 1924, I. Curie and F. Joliot made a discovery that has had very far-reaching implications. These two French scientists observed that when comparatively light elements such as boron, magnesium or aluminium are bombarded with alpha particles they themselves become radioactive, at least for a time, after the irradiation is stopped. That is to say, the natural atom of the element is converted into an artificial radioactive isotope. This remarkable finding was followed up with great energy by numbers of physicists in many parts of the world. Attempts to "stir up" the nuclei of the atoms of various elements were not restricted to bombarding them with alpha particles alone. Neutrons, protons, gamma rays and other types of energy capable of penetrating the shell of orbital electrons and reaching the nucleus were used. Today, about five hundred different artificial isotopes have been made by these types of operations.

When an alpha particle or some other extraneous object is shot into the tightly packed nucleus of an atom it disturbs the balance of forces that normally keep the atom together. These forces are strong. Indeed, up till the present generation it had never been known that it was possible to disrupt them. That is why throughout the history of chemical science until the present day, gold has always been gold no matter what chemical operations have been done upon it, and nitrogen has always been nitrogen. Today, as we have just seen, nitrogen when attacked—not by chemical but by *physical* means—becomes oxygen. But what we are now saying is that on many occasions before the attacked nucleus settles down after being bombarded, it throws off various types of radiation itself for a while. These may be electrons (that is "beta particles"), alpha particles, gamma rays or particles not found under natural conditions at all called "positrons," which are electrons carrying a positive instead of the usual negative charge.

The length of time that various artificially radioactive isotopes continue to "fizz" and give off radiation varies very much. For example, iron as it occurs in nature is made up of four non-radioactive isotopes with the atomic weights 54, 56, 57 and 58. When the nuclei of iron atoms are disturbed by irradiation, three new isotopes are produced. One of these has an atomic weight of 53: it is itself radioactive but half its radio-activity fades away in just under 9 minutes. This is called its "half-life." The second artificial isotope has an atomic weight of 59 and its half-life is 47 days. The third new isotope of iron produced by bombardment of the nucleus has an atomic weight of 55 and it goes on radiating for about 4 years before it loses half its original activity.

The radioactive isotopes of carbon have been of considerable interest, and they demonstrate at the same time the way in which the production of such isotopes—which is an achieve-ment of physics—has had an important bearing on chemistry and on other sciences. The element carbon is made up in nature of two stable isotopes with atomic weights 12 and 13. When its nucleus is irradiated three new isotopes appear; one of atomic weight 10 and half-life about 9 seconds; one of atomic weight 11 and half-life about 20 minutes; and the last C^{14} with a half-life of some five thousand years!

A very small but measurable proportion of the carbon mak-ing up the carbon dioxide of the atmosphere is composed of the radioactive isotope C^{14}. This is continuously formed from bom-bardment by cosmic rays so that the proportion remains sub-stantially constant in spite of the continuous slow decay of the active carbon atoms. It follows from this that the carbon struc-ture of plants or, for that matter, of the animals that eat the plants, also contains a fixed proportion of radioactive C^{14}. When, however, a living creature dies, the C^{14} in its tissues is no longer being replenished and consequently their radio-activity becomes slowly less. It is therefore possible by measur-ing the radioactivity of a carbon-containing object of archeo-logical interest to estimate its age provided it is somewhere between, say, 2,000 and 30,000 years old.

Radioactive isotopes of all kinds are now being used to elucidate complex chemical reactions. For example, the for-mation of sugars in the green leaves of plants out of the carbon dioxide of the atmosphere involves a complicated chain of biochemical changes. These were outlined in Chapter 8. The way that some of this knowledge was acquired was by using CO_2 made up of the identifiable—or as it is called the "labelled" —C^{14} isotope. After a fixed length of time the plant juices were analysed and some of the various organic substances isolated from them. By using a Geiger-Muller counter those which contained the C^{14} could be discovered and hence the chemical route by which the sugar is elaborated worked out.

Radioactive carbon is not the only isotope used in this way. Radioactive iodine is used to study the functioning of the thyroid gland, which synthesises iodine-containing substances in the body. Another example is the use of a radioactive isotope of lead in investigating the uptake of lead by plants. The uses of "labelled" radioactive atoms in all sorts of problems of chemical analysis and synthesis are, indeed, widespread today and have accelerated to a very large degree the pace of chemical knowledge and discovery.

But although the discovery of natural isotopes by Soddy in 1913, and the further discovery in 1933 of the manner in which they differed from each other in having different numbers of neutrons in their nuclei, were elegant and interesting advances in pure knowledge they were only the beginning. And the knowledge of how to make new and radioactive isotopes was also, of itself, only of middling significance. As we have just seen, these "labelled" atoms made artificially by the physicists have been useful to the chemists in their studies of chemical structure and, particularly, in medical chemistry. But the big advance in human affairs has been the use of atomic reactions as a source of power. This discovery—a milestone in human history—has supplemented chemical energy, and to some degree superseded it.

The whole thing started with Einstein in 1905. By abstruse calculations he reached the conclusion that mass (which is vulgarly interpreted as weight) can be related to energy. From this it was deduced that nuclear energies were millions of times greater than chemical energies. Thirty-three years later, in 1938, it was discovered that when the heavy element uranium, of atomic weight 238, was bombarded with neutrons it was split almost in half—one of the "fission" products was barium, of atomic weight 137. At the same time between two and three neutrons were released for each one striking home in the original bombardment. Natural uranium, however, is made up of three isotopes, U^{234}, U^{235}, and U^{238}, and it was soon discovered that the uranium that split up under bombardment was the U^{235} isotope. If enough of this is purified and gathered together, once the fission reaction starts, the extra neutrons released as each atom splits set off two or three more atoms and the whole thing blows up—in fact, there is an atomic explosion. This does not happen with natural uranium since the unreactive isotopes absorb the spare neutrons.

Before atomic energy can be released, therefore, it is necessary to separate U^{235} from the other uranium isotopes with which it is mixed. This is an elaborate and difficult matter. Isotopes are by definition chemically identical with each other, so it is impossible to separate one from another by chemical means. In the initial scramble in 1943 to prepare enough U^{235} to make atomic bombs, two processes were devised. The first was an electromagnetic process in which by spinning uranium in a magnetic field it was found possible to make its isotopes follow slightly separated paths. The second process was based on the fact that U^{235} vapour will diffuse through sub-microscopic holes at a somewhat different rate from U^{238}. Great plants with thousands of square feet of appropriately permeable screens were set up, together with the necessary pumps and piping to deal with millions of cubic feet of corrosive vapourised uranium.

The active isotope U^{235} is never prepared completely pure or it would not be possible to handle it. Enough non-fissile isotope or other non-explosive diluent is left to avoid premature detonation. Two such pieces may, however, be used, one at each end of a long bomb. When they are brought together, the concentration of neutron radiation builds up to such a degree that the reaction "runs away" and the bomb explodes (Fig. 65).

Since the 1940s it has been found possible to release the energy of atomic fission gradually and not in one great unmanageable run-away explosion. This has been done by arranging for the fissile isotope U^{235} to be appropriately diluted by other material capable of absorbing some of the neutrons. When fission takes place in U^{235}, heat is released and it is this heat that is used to produce power in atomic power stations.

FIG. 65.   An atom-bomb explosion

In fact, the energy of the *physical* reaction of nuclear fission is used to run steam turbines in much the same way as the energy of the *chemical* reaction between carbon and oxygen is used in conventional coal-fueled power stations.

The most important material for absorbing neutrons when natural uranium is used as fuel is, as I have already mentioned, the non-fissile U^{238} isotope. When this substance is struck by a neutron it becomes radioactive, shoots off an electron and decays to form plutonium which itself, like U^{235}, is fissile. The process of enriching natural uranium, which is made up of 0·7 per cent. of active U^{235} and 99·3 per cent. of non-fissile U^{238}, is difficult and expensive. And if only partly enriched uranium by itself is used as fuel, the fission reaction producing heat soon comes to a stop because most of the neutrons which fly off when the U^{235} atoms split up strike U^{238} atoms and are absorbed, and only a few strike other U^{235} atoms and split them and continue the process. The continuous development of energy from partly enriched uranium (enriched enough, that is, but not so much as to blow up) is made possible by using graphite (that is carbon), hydrogen, heavy hydrogen (that is deuterium) or beryllium as *moderators*. These substances impede the flying neutrons set off by the fission of U^{235}. They get hot by being thus struck and the heat, of course, is useful; but more important is the fact that the moderator causes the neutrons to slow down and ricochet about the pile, as it were, so that more of them strike U^{235} atoms and, if things are properly managed, the chain reaction continues instead of stopping.

Besides the fuel element and the moderator, the remaining essential component of an atomic energy unit is the material used for cooling. This carries away the energy resulting from the breakdown of the atomic nuclei and passes it on, as heat, to the coils carrying the water that is eventually, as steam, to drive the dynamos that produce the electricity which is the ultimate object of the whole operation. At the Calder Hall power plant, where rods of uranium are set in a matrix of graphite moderator, the heat is carried away by carbon dioxide gas circulated by blowers. The carbon dioxide becomes heated up to 336° C. and in turn, passing over water tubes, it produces steam at pressures up to 200 lb. per sq. in. to feed the turbines that drive the electricity generators (Fig. 66). In Canada, heavy water, D_2O, is being used as a combined moderator and cooling fluid, and it heats the ordinary "light" water providing steam for the turbines. At Dounreay, where highly enriched U^{235} is being used as fuel, it is essential to have a highly efficient cooling liquid to draw off the heat from this more violent nuclear reaction before the containers holding the fuel become so hot that they melt. Neither a gas like carbon dioxide, nor a liquid like water can carry the heat away fast enough. Instead, an alloy of molten metallic sodium and potassium is being used.

All this is the higher physics of nuclear anatomy, together

Fig. 66.   Calder Hall

with some more conventional physics of heat conductance and heat transfer. Chemistry comes into the problem at a technical level. Finding the appropriate chemical composition for the materials to make the different parts of an atomic pile raises quite new problems of chemical analysis. But the real significance for chemistry as we have known it in the world up to the present is that now, by using this new knowledge of the nature of the atoms of which these heavy elements are composed we can for the first time produce at will power by other than chemical means.

Up till now the main sources of power have all been chemical. The industrial and scientific revolution in which we have been living got into its stride early in the nineteenth century with the invention of the steam engine. This of course, depends basically on the chemical reaction by which the carbon of coal is oxidised and becomes carbon dioxide, thus:

$$C \quad + \quad O_2 \quad \longrightarrow \quad CO_2$$

Carbon   Oxygen   Carbon dioxide

Following the steam engine which produced power directly, and the electric dynamo which came as a secondary source of power itself dependent on steam power, there came the internal combustion engine. The most superficial glance at international politics is enough to show that all modern industrial nations need petroleum to keep the complex of their manufacture and transport in operation. Here again the basic drive is chemical. Again it is the release of power from reduced carbon and hydrogen by the chemical process of oxidation. The problems of octane ratings and anti-knock and the diversity of machines used to harness the power produced—ranging from the largest diesel plants for driving ships all the way down a two-stroke motor lawnmower—are mere matters of detail. Behind it all is the chemical reaction:

$$2C_nH_{n+2} \quad + \quad (2\tfrac{1}{2}n + 1)O_2 \quad \longrightarrow \quad 2nCO_2 \quad + \quad (n + 2)H_2O$$

Hydrocarbon   Oxygen   Carbon dioxide   Water

Now with increasing amounts of atomic power in sight to add to the comparatively trivial supplies of energy from water and the negligible quantities from wind (since sailing ships have come to an end), it is possible to visualise the valuable supplies of "banked" reduced carbon (I refer to coal and oil) being used to make useful carbon-built things—textiles, plastics, tyres or what you will—with which we have already made a proper start in this present generation, rather than so much being burned as fuel. This is the main contribution to chemistry of our new knowledge and command of the atomic nucleus.

There are, of course, new possibilities for the future. The production of power by means of a steam engine had to await the development of engineering skill to machine pistons that would fit the cylinders of the engine reasonably accurately. Similarly, the fixation of nitrogen and the polymerisation of ethylene required initially the development of equipment for very high pressure reactions. In other words, many chemical reactions require extreme conditions of temperature and pressure which can only be provided for by advances in technology. In the same way, it has been known since 1934 that certain nuclear reactions were theoretically possible, but they have only been achieved in practice since we have had sufficient knowledge to make nuclear fission explosions take place.

It was many years ago that it was first recognised that it might be possible to cause the nuclei of certain light elements to fuse together and release energy, just as it is possible to cause the nuclei of uranium and some other heavy elements to split apart. A paper was published on this in Vienna by Hans Thirring in 1946.

In chemistry, a matchstick has to be heated, at atmospheric pressure, up to about 700° C. before it bursts into flame and the carbon spontaneously "fuses" with atmospheric oxygen—at the level of electron shells, of course, and not on a nuclear basis. Similarly, though at a quite different level of intensity, if isotopes of hydrogen are heated to the immense temperature produced by an "ordinary" atomic bomb, their nuclei can be made to fuse and it is possible to make the fusion continue (just like a burning match) until all the ingredients are "burned" up. It is reported that one of the American "hydrogen fusion" bombs produced two hundred times as much energy as the uranium fission bomb that killed and injured 133,000 people in Hiroshima (nearly half of them were killed). The most suitable ingredients for nuclear *fusion* are the two heavy isotopes of hydrogen shown in Fig. 67 side by side with hydrogen as it normally is.

The controlled release of energy from nuclear fusion (as distinct from fission) has only just been announced on an experimental basis. There seems no reason, however, to doubt that in due course it will be harnessed to industrial uses. We shall then have an even more fruitful source of non-chemical energy. Besides this, it may be possible to produce useful elements otherwise difficult to get by joining the nuclei of small atoms, just as today some new elements are derived from breaking down the large elements used in atomic piles.

The development of our present understanding of the principles upon which chemistry is based has brought us to a

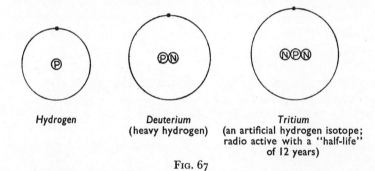

| Hydrogen | Deuterium (heavy hydrogen) | Tritium (an artificial hydrogen isotope; radio active with a "half-life" of 12 years) |

FIG. 67

remarkable understanding of the detailed anatomy of the atoms of all the difficult elements we know on earth. But this knowledge has led us away from the sort of chemistry which we usually think of as chemical. The H_2O, H_2SO_4 business, the combination of acids and alkalis to produce salts, all the detail of the chemical textbooks, is important and must still be learnt by anyone who wants to be known as a chemist. But the explanation of these things has moved out of chemistry into physics. And in physics, in place of the many different elements, the metals, the rare earths, the carbon compounds and all the rest, we have a few ultimate particles. There are the close-knit heavy protons and neutrons making up the atomic nucleus, and circling around these in wide orbits like the rings of Saturn are the various shells of revolving electrons (Fig. 68).

This insight into the structure of the atom has enabled us to

understand the inter-relationship between the different elements that make up the periodic table of Mendeléev. Ultimately, the laws of chemical combination are explicable in
terms of physics—although many of us lesser chemists may continue for a while to learn up the behaviour of the different substances we meet as they are still set out in the textbooks. Knowledge about electrons, first discovered in 1897, by which
chemical atoms are linked together, has enabled us to control
streams of them in cathode-ray tubes and in the multiplicity of
radio valves and rectifiers and photoelectric cells. Besides giving

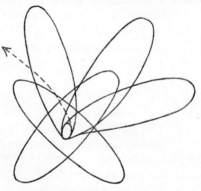

Fig. 68.   Lithium atom

us entertainment and means of communication and sensitive
methods of controlling industrial operations, this new technology of *electronics* has made possible the modern electronic
computer upon which the rapidly expanding development of
"automation" is based.

Command of the atomic nucleus we have already discussed.
Our knowledge of nuclear physics has given us "labelled"
isotopes as a tool for chemical research, and it gives us power
for industry—or for the annihilation of the human race.

But there is another direction in which chemistry is developing into a new field as fresh knowledge is acquired. This is the
growing understanding of the composition and structure of
large molecules. Classical chemistry dealt with acids and salts
and metals and simple compounds that could be crystallised.

The entire field of biochemistry, indeed, the very realisation that living tissues are susceptible to chemical investigation at all, is comparatively new. And the ability to construct by chemical means artificial substances, fibres, construction materials, artificial rubbers—the whole range of modern polymers—this is newest of all. But although it is a remarkable achievement, as I have tried to show in Chapter 9, it is only a beginning.

I should like in this concluding part of my book to quote something of what Professor Astbury of the University of Leeds said at a conference on "Large Molecules in Biology" held in Italy in 1955. He referred there to the various kinds of man-made fibres that have been developed "from the lessons learnt from nature; how there arose the concept of high polymers and specially of chain-molecules; and how in some sense we have even improved upon nature by synthesising brand-new chain-molecules from which we now spin such wonder fibres as nylon and terylene, and yet," said Professor Astbury, "in spite of these proud achievements, how insignificant it seems compared with the least that nature has done! Yes, those superb chain-molecules—proteins, nucleic acids, polysaccharides [that is starches and the like] and the amazing versatility with which they have been exploited in the evolution of life, must always be our truest inspiration, and time and time again we must turn to the book of nature to read anew that magnificent story."

One of the most stimulating and exciting features of being a chemist in this second half of the twentieth century is that there are today such remarkable, new and penetrating "glasses" through which to study this book of nature. The microscope was invented by Robert Hooke in about 1664 and by the great Dutchman, Antony van Leeuwenhoek, at about the same time. These men three hundred years ago first saw the microscopic world of living creatures that live all about us. Since then the existence of the atoms of chemical elements has been deduced by reasoning from stronger and stronger circumstantial evidence. Now in our own generation it has become possible—with the electron microscope—for the first time to see, if not an atom at least a single molecule. These are large molecules, "macromolecules" as we now call them, but molecules nevertheless. And the Geiger counters allow us to follow the track of single "labelled" atoms as they combine and recombine in the chemical systems into which we put them.

The great molecules—these polymers of perspex, of polythene, of terylene and the like—are indeed remarkable products of our new and developing understanding of chemistry. But, as Professor Astbury has put it, it may be that we have arrived at the right answer for the wrong reasons. For example, although our understanding of the way catalysts work is within sight of becoming a coherent system of knowledge, it has not yet emerged into a systematic and ordered codex. Nature, on the other hand, has worked out its own elegant scheme of catalysts and it is upon them that the whole of the complex chemistry of life depends for its orderly and systematic operation. The catalysts in nature are enzymes. And for each stage of a chemical transformation, for example ten or so stages from sugar to alcohol in yeast fermentation, there is a special enzyme, each one designed to do just one chemical operation. Similarly, for each stage of the building up of muscular tissue in a growing animal, the appropriate enzyme catalyst plays its part. Compared to this, even the new and remarkable Ziegler catalysts recently discovered for putting together polythene seem crude and ham-handed.

But nature has gone even further. It now seems clear that many of the polymers we find in biology—the cellulose fibres we can now see under the electron microscope, for example, which the chemists borrowed to make into their own celluloid, and artificial silk, and rayon, and the like—many of these start out in the living cell as part of the biological structure and only later finish up as "molecular yarns." The most remarkable example of this dual function in the organic chemistry of biological life are the flagallae of algae, spermatazoa and micro-organisms.

If you look through a microscope at a drop of pond water, you will see a number of simple, elementary creatures busily moving about. Under a higher-powered microscope it can be observed that what moves many of them is a fringe of what appear to be rhythmically vibrating "hairs." These are the flagellae. They are in some respects like the many oars of a Roman galley. It is now known that each of these minute organs of locomotion is a single molecule. Each is, in effect, a monomolecular muscle. This single organ, only about 120 Å thick, is one molecule of a polymer. It represents the molecular mechanism of biological mobility stripped down to its barest essentials.

This achievement of nature, this production of a large molecule, which is at one and the same time a fibre not widely dissimilar from terylene and yet which is on the other hand instinct with life and movement, is at the present moment beyond our reach as chemists. And yet, because we now have the means of "seeing" and examing its structure, because we now have radioactive probes, electron microscopes, X-ray crystallographs and all the remarkable paraphernalia of modern physics with which to scrutinise the chemical and physical make-up of such molecules, it is not beyond the bounds of possibility that chemists may in the future be able to make such things themselves.

Quite obviously there is a long way to go. We have already an inkling of the way in which nature "prints off" its new cells. In order to synthesise in the laboratory the polymer, starch, out of separate glucose units, Charles Hanes used an appropriate enzyme. This enzyme itself is chemically a protein, that is to say, it is a nitrogen-containing polymer. When a living cell gets ready to produce out of itself another living cell it uses the chemical compound deoxy-ribonucleic acid, D.N.A. I described this in Chapter 8. D.N.A. is itself a polymer. To synthesise it artificially in the laboratory is at present far beyond our reach. But the fact that Crick and Watson, using X-ray analysis, have been able to to give us a fairly definite picture of its structure—a great double corkscrew with more than a thousand twists—this at least shows us modern chemists what we are up against.

This brings me to the end of what I want to say. In this book I have tried to describe what chemistry is about. And the fact that in its immensely multifarious detail it is very complicated does not alter its underlying nature. We now know the great polymerised, organic molecules we find in nature to be vastly complex. And in biology, the fact that the biochemist knows something about the structure of the materials that make up a living cell does not yet enable the embryologist who is studying the development of a living creature to dispense with the classical methods he has used for so long. Even simple animals like frogs and earthworms are still far beyond the possibilities of chemical definition. Nevertheless, the chemist is nearer to defining them than he once was. Similarly in the field of physics, although a great deal has been discovered about the ultimate nature of the diverse elements found on earth—or, for that matter in the stars—the physicist also has some way further to go. In earlier pages I have restricted myself to talk of electrons and protons and neutrons. But, as so frequently occurs in nature, things are in truth more complex. Already, to explain the phenomena he observes, the physicist and the mathematician have recourse to photons, pions, muons, neutrinos, K-particles, sigma particles, fermions and bosons. Like the nutritionists before them who, having discovered vitamins, proceeded further and found a number of anti-vitamins, the physicists also now have their "anti-particles." There is the positron (an "anti-electron)", the "anti-proton" and the "anti-neutron." Later still it has been found necessary to wrestle with a number of new observations suggesting to the physicist that there is a further group of "queer" particles yet to be dealt with.

But behind all this advanced theory, the science of chemistry is firmly based on *observation*. I emphasised in Chapter I that the chemist can only see and weigh and measure what other men could do also. But the chemist records what he measures of the material substances around him and from these quantitative measurements he deduces the rules of behaviour of the different elements. The fact that he aids his simple senses with more and more refined instruments—with delicate balances, with spectrographs, with infra-red, and ultra-violent, and X-rays—does not alter the fact that his knowledge depends on observation. And if, from observation and deduction and thought and experiment, the modern chemist has achieved some remarkable things the reason is—as Isaac Newton wrote to Robert Hooke in 1675—that he has "seen further . . . by standing on the shoulders of Giants."

Index